CROSSING THE LINES

CROSSING THE LINES

New Writing by International Students

Edited by

Jackie Kay and Kachi A. Ozumba

FlambardPress

First published in Great Britain in 2011 by Flambard Press
Holy Jesus Hospital, City Road, Newcastle upon Tyne NE1 2AS
www.flambardpress.co.uk

Typeset by BookType
Cover Design by Gainford Design Associates
Cover photograph by Richard Brocken, used courtesy of Echo Images

Printed in Great Britain by Bell & Bain, Glasgow

A CIP catalogue record for this book is available from the British Library.

ISBN: 9781906601263

Flambard Press wishes to thank Arts Council England
for its financial support.

Flambard Press is a member of Inpress.

The paper used for this book is FSC accredited

Contents

Introduction

International students have been part of the fabric of British life for many years. Every year hundreds of thousands of hopeful students cross land and sea, travelling vast distances, to pursue their education here. These students make as much impact on their community as their community makes on them. A university town becomes richer and more diverse from the wide cultural intake of international students. And towns up and down the country are introduced to fresh, open, intelligent eyes, with new ways of seeing their host city.

In January 2010, the Newcastle Centre for the Literary Arts (NCLA) launched the UK International Student Short Story Competition, primarily because we thought it would be interesting to read short stories written from the vantage point of the newcomer, the outsider and the newly arrived, and glean from their varied experiences new ways of seeing the old country. After all, some of the best of our world literature comes from writers who have felt as if they didn't belong to their country, from people in exile, from people on the borders and those living in the margins. We wanted to attract students across a range of disciplines, not just Creative Writing or English, and give them an opportunity to assess and translate their experiences creatively.

To our delight, many students submitted stories from more than twenty-six universities. We've picked what we thought were the best stories from a brilliant and energising collection. We didn't have a specific brief. We didn't want the students to feel obliged to write about their student experience, or to feel like they had to write particularly autobiographically. We were interested in fresh and original stories, which had the smack of authenticity to them. We were fascinated to see what characters would be created from this experience, what points of view would be taken. We weren't disappointed. Here are stories, wide-ranging and unexpected in their themes, from first responses to the snow to first experiences of obsessive love; from the discovery of fierce friendships to the abjectness of dejected loneliness; from the discovery of chocolate to the discovery of drugs. The characters in these stories experience the ups and downs of the newly arrived. They are as likely to feel the intense need to fit in as they are to want to be a recluse. These stories pointedly explore what it means to belong and what it means not to belong. Tender, warm, funny and passionate, the stories in this collection will make the reader think. 'Foreigners' often offer fresh and funny perspectives on society that only they could have, seeing the mores and the traditions of British culture in a unique and hilarious way. Many stories here too contain classic culture clashes.

The contributors to this collection have all come to Britain from diverse countries in the continents of Africa, Asia, Australia, North America and South America. Their disciplines range from Medicine, Engineering and Law to Business Management and Creative Writing.

We hope this anthology contributes to the existing literature about the UK international student experience, and provides useful insights not only to schools, agencies and people involved in teaching international students, and prospective international students, but also to the students themselves. For them we hope that this collection might provoke a laugh of recognition and some welcome company in the first weeks and months in a new and often daunting country. But more than anything, we hope that you enjoy these stories, as we have done, and that they might inspire you or compel you to get writing your own!

Jackie Kay
Kachi A. Ozumba

Chinese Seasons in the Heart of England

Alan Islas-Cital

Mexico/University of Birmingham

It was my addiction to new beginnings that brought me to the English West Midlands. I was hell-bent on forgetting and starting anew, entangled in a precarious cycle of despair and determination that lasted for decades and that, at the time of my first trip to Europe, filled me with excitement over the prospect of radical change.

I was going to England after all, a country with a lofty reputation in my native Mexico, even when the majority picture it as a misty island of punctuality, medieval knights, hooligans, a lingering royalty, and larger-than-life rock stars. All in all, the prevailing perception of Great Britain (or England, or the United Kingdom – few really knew the difference) was formed from superficial and often contradictory notions that in my part of the world, nonetheless, amounted to a sense of awe.

On the other hand, Ensenada, the place where I was born, is a relatively small coastal town located 100 km south from the infamous Tijuana, and sitting lazily in a bay of the peninsula of Baja California facing the Pacific Ocean. It is a simple fishing town that grew around a Wild-West-style *cantina* with swinging doors and all, and where fat *mariachis* still sing depressing songs of loss and betrayal. No glamour in Ensenada, no Freddy Mercury, no Oasis, no Ozzy Osbourne, but even so, I loved that place fiercely and without even knowing it.

Among my first impressions of England, the grass was what amazed me the most. As I travelled by coach from London to Birmingham, I leaned my head against the window and just looked at the grass. Half sleeping and dizzy with exhaustion, I saw the swift passage of vast green extensions curved in gentle slopes, and dotted by fluffy personalities of ever-chewing sheep. For me it was strangely nostalgic, as it was a landscape directly drawn from the huge jigsaw puzzles that my mother used to put together during idle afternoons. Everywhere I found this strange familiarity, similar to a dream in which everything seems normal apart from disquieting details that should not be so – jagged fragments of the unexpected.

For Tiexin, on the other hand, the UK was all decidedly alien. She had no prior exposure to the West other than what could be gleaned from Hollywood movies, and had never ventured beyond China before. Her father had been a soldier in the People's Army and she had grown up in the closed community of the barracks, breathing nationalism and taking to heart the official dogma. Her native city, Luo Yang, located in the central province of Henan, had been the capital of several ancient dynasties, and it persisted there, enduring periodic floods from the Yellow River over the centuries, its surrounding of hazy old mountains straight out of a classical Asian painting.

Then there was the language Great Wall. Her first encounters in the real setting of an English-speaking country were not so bad, but not free from confusion and often absurd misunderstandings. For example, she was initially surprised by what she thought was an inordinate number of toilets scattered everywhere, which turned out to be 'to let' signs instead.

Her name was Tiexin Ouyan, and she was doing a PhD in Metallurgy and Materials in the same university as me. She was studying the microstructure that arises in titanium alloys after they have been welded by vigorous rubbing, in a process that goes by the technical name of Linear Friction Welding. When asked about her research, she would say, 'I work on the design of jet engines, making flying safer,' which was not completely untrue as the welding was used to attach blades to disks in rotors. Many PhD students used such strategies to lift the status of their research before the eyes of uncaring strangers. For my part, I often resorted to dolphins, submarines and sunken treasure when talking about my involvement in underwater acoustics and sonar. In reality, I used heavy metallic spheres as calibration targets, painstakingly tying them in supporting nylon nets, and bouncing sound pulses from them. For me, and for most of the PhD students I knew, there was no more glamour in our research than the gala nights of the few conferences we managed to attend from time to time.

Tiexin and I met at one of those events aimed at

getting PhD students out from their musty labs and desks. In those days I had a nagging feeling that there was something horribly wrong with my life. I was convinced that I had drifted into inertia somewhere along the road. As a reaction, I tried to occupy myself with various activities. I attended everything that was available, every course, workshop, lecture and event happening nearby. I took yoga classes, practised drawing, got a pool membership and went for swimming lessons, joined the hiking club, ran a marathon for charity, attended meetings of the debating society and so forth. I was desperate for meaning, but ultimately what I got was an escape.

This was the state of my mind when I first saw her. We coincided at the buffet table, filling our plates with sandwiches while balancing our drinks. She smiled, her face a portrait of happiness and anachronistic innocence. I was a bit taken aback and did not regard her as particularly pretty or charming. 'A little girl,' I thought, 'a little Chinese girl.' Of course I could not have predicted it then, but she was exactly what I needed, a precise fit for my fears and shortcomings. She was the answer for me, a little Chinese girl eating sandwiches and laughing without any mysteries whatsoever.

This was our life when we began to fall in love. She spent most of her evenings trying to make sense out of the blurry screen of an electronic microscope, playing Chinese pop songs against the silence of an old empty building. Meanwhile, I sat in front of my computer without enthusiasm, surrounded by a ridiculous volume of scientific papers stacked high and gathering dust. We both struggled to rekindle the motivation for research and curiosity for discovery, but life was not easy or exuberant, or even happy.

Our relationship grew quickly. After a few weeks I was calling her every day and we were having lunch together more and more frequently. She made me laugh and I was never afraid of getting stuck in awkward silence. Even in our imperfect English we somehow managed to communicate and talk about all kinds of things. I learnt about a civilisation that encompassed millennia, its long history and the small facts of everyday life, from the legendary age of the Three Kingdoms to the familiarity of school-morning exercise. In Tiexin I had gained an unconditional ally. She would ring me at six in the morning to make sure that I got up early. We would stay until midnight in our labs, and then eat chicken burgers from the local kebab shop. Eventually, I gained a girlfriend, officially sealed when my supervisor surprised us kissing by the laboratory water tank, to the general embarrassment of the three of us.

Winter came and we were together, braving the horrible weather with pitiful wet socks and holding our gloved cold hands. From afar, the virgin whiteness of first snow was beautiful and surreal; but actually walking on the icy mud puddles into which snow degenerated was a different matter. But we remained cheerful. The moment was enough, the evenings spent in my room serenaded by the rain while watching old kung-fu movies, the precious loneliness of a campus that seemed to be only ours, the unapologetic heaviness of a full-English breakfast, the secret gardens with derelict ponds where we had lunch sometimes. We took trips in the top floor of double-decker buses, exploring the suburbs and discovering ancient buildings, mosques, charming cemeteries and traditional pubs, cosy and crooked under the weight of their ancestral timber. Slowly, the days regained meaning and a path, a joyous routine where work also had a place, began to emerge.

Unfortunately, not everything came so smoothly. For one thing, we had contrasting personalities. I was the dreamy kind of procrastinator, with a head full of utopias and master plans. She was the pragmatic and hard-working kind of person who puts effort, hopes and savings into a future with a house, family and steady income. Differences in culture and upbringing also had a surprising impact on our relationship. Because I had enough experience in a wildly multicultural environment, I distrusted stereotypes and racial prejudice. For example, I played Sunday football with a group of people that hardly included two from the same country, and they seldom fitted their expected moulds of demeanour (let alone football ability). From daily interaction with people from diverse countries I saw how obvious cultural differences were, but also that they were superficial. Personal disposition was much more important than the origin of a passport. Living abroad highlighted the shared condition of human nature: the fact that, essentially, we all wanted the same things.

With such an outlook, it was a bit of shock when I found it extremely challenging to connect with Tiexin's Chinese friends. They tended to speak Mandarin most of the time, even when I was there. On greeting them, I felt they were cold or even rude, often ignoring me and always lacking the loud manners of Mexicans bumping into each other in the street. I missed the excesses of male physical contact, which in my circle were the staple of close and true friendship. And when we conversed, they came across to me as savagely focused on material success, almost obsessed with attending prestigious universities and landing well-paid jobs. This strong drive for getting ahead in the world was, of course, a positive trait; but to my nebulous idealist sensibilities, it resounded as empty, devoid of a deeper significance. While I was restraining myself from generalizing about Chinese students and giving up on socialising with Tiexin's Chinese friends, the truth was that, other than Tiexin, I had not developed a close relationship with any Chinese.

A couple of our first fights were in part an extension of this cultural clash, with the Dalai Lama being the unlikely source. I, who had chanted 'Free Tibet' in the streets, with long hair and raised fist, could not easily accept what she explained to me about the Chinese perspective on this conflict. She was convinced that the smiling monk and spiritual leader, also a recipient of a Nobel Peace Prize, was in reality a scheming old man taking advantage of the natural religiosity of the Tibetan people in order to grab power. I could not digest this idea. It seemed to me just outrageous and plainly wrong. More than once I walked away from her, both of us fuming. This was repeated every time we discussed the latest news from the Chinese government and their actions, alleged or otherwise.

'You believe everything from the Western media,' she would say.

'You have been brainwashed,' I would retort.

But we managed to work out those issues. Our mutual intransigencies eventually subsided as we tried to listen, to understand, to find a middle way. It was not easy, but we tried.

We were still together after the end of that winter, when the cold gave way to a shaky warmth. During spring and summer the English students only needed the faintest hint of a sunny day to get out the sandals and short pants. Spontaneous picnics appeared and multiplied under the trees, among the squirrels. Tiexin and I struggled to maintain a disciplined routine because the days were far too beautiful and tempting to stay indoors. We indulged in countryside trips to the Peak District, the Malvern Hills and North Wales. We celebrated my twenty-ninth birthday in a small town in Gloucestershire called Painswick and nicknamed 'The Queen of the Cotswolds'. There, I realised that I wanted to go everywhere with her, see places, have dinner, wake up together. We started to think about the future and considered looking for a place to live together. In Birmingham, I had been in shared student houses for two years, most of the time holed up in my room. I had been unlucky with my housemates, who turned out to be truly monstrous. They were the kind who thrived in disgusting kitchens and noxious bathrooms, sleeping happily all day among beer cans in the aftermath of raucous parties. I was tired and peeved with this situation. I felt trapped and longed to have a place of my own where I could truly relax and be able to roam around in my underwear if I so wished. But most of all, I wanted to live with Tiexin.

We were approaching decisions that could alter our lives radically and permanently. I was terrified of the definitive, too used to saying to myself, 'There is time, if it goes badly it can be fixed.' But time was no longer abundant, and whatever my choices were now, they would become my destiny. It felt premature to address the future at this stage, as for most other couples it would certainly be. However, in our particular circumstance we had to think about what would happen if we went ahead and got married. Where would we live? What would happen with our respective families? We were from worlds apart, we did not speak each other's languages, and we were struggling to finish hard PhDs in a country that was foreign to both of us. It was harsh and we had no idea of what would happen in the end.

We were still together in autumn. Through the window of our room entered a light tinged with hues of sepia. Outside, the branches of a tree moved back and forth rhythmically, a surf of stubborn leaves. She was reading on the desk, singing softly an old song in Mandarin. I was in bed, briefly without worries or desires, looking at her hair, listening to her voice amidst the mellow ruffling of the world.

When the Chips are Down

Ayodele Morocco-Clarke

Nigeria/University of Aberdeen

Lectures were hell this morning and the afternoon shift at my part-time job at the Tube station was worse. The day is, however, far from over as I have to do another shift at my other part-time job.

I hurry across from the station with my university friend Pete who also has a part-time job at the station. He latches on to something I said while we were getting our coats.

'What do you mean you'd rather be cold than hot? You are from bloody Africa.'

'And so what?' I throw back at him in annoyance. 'What has my being from Africa got to do with me preferring the cold to the heat?'

'This is what happens when all you people migrate from your various countries to the West. You always attempt to deny your former existence. How can you prefer the cold when all your life you have been in the sun? You have spent less than a year here, yet you are attempting to be more English than we the English.'

I glare at Pete. At five feet four inches, he is vertically challenged and feels the need to constantly assert his opinion in an obnoxious manner, as if that makes up for his being so small. Everyone agrees that Pete suffers from 'Short-Man Syndrome'. For a man, he has tiny hands and feet, and a torso that seems strangely large when compared to his short stumpy legs. The overall effect is the askew look of someone who was created in haste, and his sharp dress sense does little to assuage this fact.

I decide not to be drawn into another argument and instead glance at my watch impatiently. At this rate, I am once again going to be late for my second job.

In typical Pete style, he is unwilling to let go once he has sunk his gnashers into a disagreement. 'I was here when you saw snow for the first time; suddenly you have become the ice man.'

I pretend to be engrossed in sending a text message, though I can see him through my peripheral vision. His comically large nose, flaring with each inhalation of air, is almost beetroot-red at the tip. He slaps his hands together in a bid to infuse some heat from one palm to another. Exasperatingly, the weather is a maximum of ten to twelve degrees centigrade in April, which, by and large, should be the spring season – but clearly is not – and we have spent the last thirty-five minutes at the bus-stop adjacent to the Angel Tube station waiting for bus 30 after concluding our shifts at the station.

'I'd rather be cold than hot,' he continues to mimic in a ridiculous accent.

I know I sound nothing like that and, to be honest, he is really getting on my nerves. I consider walking to the next bus-stop to get away from him, deciding instead to hop on whatever bus comes next, irrespective of destination.

'Maybe you should move to the North Pole since you like the cold so much,' he carries on.

'Shut up, Pete.'

'Well, I'm serious. How can you say you prefer the cold to the heat when you have spent all your life in the tropics? Why are you trying to deny who you really are? You are like all those other foreigners who try to blend into their new environment by eradicating all original traces of their home country. It's like you people feel that you need to whiten yourselves and suck up to us in order to validate your existence.'

'And you came to this conclusion just from me saying that I prefer the cold to the heat, huh?'

'That is how it starts.'

'You are so full of crap, Pete. It's no wonder that only very few people can bear to be around you. Yes, I was born and bred in Nigeria. For your information, Africa is not a country. Yes, I spent all my life there, but there is one thing you have to understand: I have experienced the heat and I have experienced the cold, and I know which I prefer. There are millions of English people who would rather be hot than cold or who would prefer a hot sunny climate, and this includes you. I do not see you saying that you all are trying to "Africanise" yourselves. I do not see you saying that you are not true to who you are.'

His eyes widen in disbelief, making him look like a caricature, while his mouth works furiously yet soundlessly. For the first time since I have known him, he is dumbstruck. I have never spoken to him like this before and I can see that, uncharacteristically, he is taking a while to gather his thoughts.

Spurred on by weeks of frustration and his scathing tongue, I am not about to quit. 'You are very rude and you think the fact that you have this massive boulder lodged firmly on your shoulder gives you the right to speak to people any way you want. You need to learn some manners. You annoy me so much that I don't even want to be around you,' I snap as I lunge past the closing doors of one of the two 38 buses that have stopped before us.

I can still see the shock on his face long after the bus has pulled away. I feel a small pang of guilt which is soon washed away as I struggle to keep my balance whilst being squashed among the bodies of other passengers. I start to re-plan my journey route to incorporate my detour on bus 38. I shall alight on Mare Street and sprint to the Old Kenton pub where I work in the evenings. I curse under my breath – I am going to be more than a little late.

Shirley glowers at me as I dash into the pub to take up my position behind the bar. 'DJ, this cannot continue. It seems you do not like this job. If you do not take this job seriously, we can get someone else to replace you.'

I stare incredulously at the woman. We? Who does she think she is? First of all, she is not my boss. Secondly, my name is not DJ and I hasten to remind her of this.

'My name is not DJ. It is Deji . . . Dayyy-Jeee. Got it?'

'Whatever! To-may-toe, to-mah-toe.'

'That's not the same and you know it. I've told you DJ is not my name. The next time you call me DJ, I will ignore you.' I am really wound up.

I set to clearing the glasses from tables after serving a few punters.

Shirley screeches at me, 'DJ, the Foster's barrel needs changing. Can you do it now?'

It is more an order than a request. What irks me is that we have both been employed to do the same job. Just because she is sexually involved with the pub landlord, she feels she can throw her weight around.

The stress of the whole day is catching up with me and I am pretty close to breaking point. But since I need the extra income, I cannot afford to lose this job. So taking a deep breath, I rein in my temper and put on a sweet smile. Two can play this game. 'Sure, Sheila. I'll change it right away,' I respond.

'Who are you calling Sheila?' she snaps.

I shrug and say 'To-may-toe, to-mah-toe,' as I go to the basement to change the barrel.

When I take my place behind the counter, Shirley looks like she is about to burst a blood vessel. 'You think you are so smart, DJ.'

'Are you talking to me, Sheila?' I respond gaily.

'Stop calling me Sheila,' she screeches.

'Stop calling me DJ,' I say sweetly.

I can see a vein in her temple ticking. As usual, her hair is pulled back in a severe bun, giving her eyes a slightly oriental look and tightening any loose skin in the style popularly known as a Croydon facelift. I ignore her for the rest of the night but notice that she keeps out of my way. The few times she needed to draw my attention, she struggled to call me Deji. I had made my point.

The next day at university I give Pete a wide berth, and the following day at the Tube station, I do my best to avoid him during the rush-hour ticket inspection. I keep expecting him to shimmy up to me with an accusation over my abominable behaviour of two days before, but he keeps his distance even when he sees me having a difficult time with an aggressive ticket dodger. He would normally have come over to give me a helping hand but remains aloof, efficiently minding his patch, pretending not to see anything untoward. I am a little disappointed. He is actually my closest ally in this dreadful place.

By lunchtime, I am weary of the silence between us. I regret being nasty to him but unwilling to lose face I strike up a new alliance with Jimmy. I have always been friendly with him at the station but my close-ness to Pete proved effective in keeping him at arm's length as he considers Pete 'an arrogant bastard'. I, however, know that this is Pete's way of dealing with his shortcomings. We all have our different survival mechanisms, only most of us realise that there are other people to consider.

At the close of work, I head off in the company of Jimmy and a few of the other work guys. I see Pete at the bus stop. He is already waiting for a bus by the time we get there and stands all alone like a Billy-no-mates, causing me to feel bad for a while. I am however enjoying the company of the guys I am hanging out with and ignore him. When bus 30 pulls up, I say my goodbyes and board the bus behind Pete. He goes upstairs as we usually do, while I decide to take a seat downstairs at the rear end of the bus.

My banter with my workmates notwithstanding, I am in a foul mood by the time I alight from the bus. It has been another long day and I have to contend with extra hours stuck in an enclosed place with Shirley. At least she cannot complain that I am late today. Knowing her, though, she will make sure there are other things to whine about. I struggle through my chores and not soon enough it is closing time.

The next day being a Saturday, I have to cover a shift at the pub. Although I was not originally scheduled to work, I welcome the extra income the shift will generate and hasten to arrive there in good time. I am kept thoroughly occupied by the punters thronging into the pub. Today is the North London derby football match between Arsenal and Tottenham Hotspur. There is a raucous crowd of drunken fanatics chanting, singing, groaning, cursing, bemoaning, yelling and spilling their pints of lager. We are taking lots of money at the till and the customers are generous with their tips, or so engrossed in the game that many walk off without collecting their change.

The Arsenal mob is gathered at one end of the pub, with the Spurs crowd occupying the other end. The pub is heaving with people, making it almost impossible to weave among them when I need to retrieve glasses and bottles. There is much animosity between the opposing fans and the tension is palpable, denser even than the cigarette smoke threatening to choke the life out of me.

Though there are lots of chances created, neither

of the teams have scored by the end of the first half, leaving every single fan disgruntled. Most people walk outside for some fresh air while dissecting and analysing every aspect of the game, ruing opportunities missed. The first half has been dominated by Spurs, leaving the Arsenal supporters doubly aggrieved over the decision of their manager to leave their iconic goal-scoring talisman, Thierry Henry, and the young playmaker, Cesc Fabregas, on the substitution bench, citing this as the bane of the performance by their beloved team during the first half of the game.

Apparently, this match is important to both teams in the race for who will finish fourth in the English Premier League. The Spurs group have the upper hand. Having dominated the first forty-five minutes of the game, they have smelt blood and waste no time in mocking the Arsenal crowd over the incompetence of their team. As the kick-off of the second half starts, there are a few scuffles, though nothing particularly violent.

The second half of the game sees Arsenal emerge as the dominant team. The situation improves further for the Arsenal fans when their manager makes some tactical substitution and introduces both Thierry Henry and Fabregas almost simultaneously. Shortly after this, things threaten to boil over when Tottenham score. Arsenal players accuse them of cheating and poor gamesmanship as play should have been stopped when one of their players went down. Spurs fans are jubilant. There is a deafening roar accompanied by lots of back-slapping, with the Spurs fans pointing at the Arsenal fans and chanting over and over, 'Who are ya! Who are ya! Who are ya!'

Incensed, the Arsenal lot try their best to ignore the Spurs fans, finding reprieve when Henry scores an equalising goal a few minutes from full time. Now it is the Arsenal supporters' turn to taunt their opponents. By this time, I am once again slowly, carefully weaving my way among people, collecting glasses and emptying ashtrays. Many people are so engrossed in the game that my shouting 'Excuse me' goes ignored, prompting me to elbow my way across the room.

Clumsily, I tread on someone's foot, causing the owner of the foot to shove me and send me crashing into several other people. Now, I am not a slight man in the least and it is not easy to right myself, especially clutching on to several pint glasses and a few ashtrays. I am in the Spurs section and the fans are not so forgiving, especially after seeing victory snatched out of their grasp a few moments earlier. The people I have careened into turn on me with vengeance.

Things take a turn for the worse when I try to defend myself. Very quickly, a ring has opened up with me in the middle and I am sprawled on the floor amidst broken glass being pummelled, stomped on and kicked over and over. I can see blood and have no recollection of the moment I let go of the glasses. I hear screams in the background, at the same time hearing some of my assailants call me a 'bloody nigger'.

I have always thought that the word 'nigger' is used as a weapon by white people against someone black, but my attackers consist of some black men and I neither see any of them pause nor hear them protest at the use of the offensive word. For all I know it could have been any of them who called me a nigger. This is my first taste of face-to-face racism since I came to the UK. My pride is almost as wounded as my battered body.

The screaming voice belongs to Shirley. A big fight breaks out as the opposing fans get involved in the melee, wrecking furniture and breaking glasses and bottles in the process. I hear sirens approaching and through my painfully swollen left eye see the pub empty with lightening speed. Shirley helps me onto one of the unbroken chairs while the landlord sees the policemen in. Thankfully, the paramedics are not far behind. I am in such agony that it hurts to take a breath. I do my breathing through my mouth. I have felt my nose and know that it is broken. My right eye is completely shut; the vision I have in my left eye can best be described as slit vision. My ribs feel like they have collapsed and my head is like an over-sized ripe pumpkin on the brink of tipping over and exploding.

Shirley sits holding my hand while I am checked out by the paramedics. She looks genuinely concerned about my wellbeing and appears shaken by the events of the day. She offers to go with me in the ambulance to Homerton hospital. This is a side to Shirley I have never seen before.

Upon extensive examination and X-rays, it is confirmed, as I have feared, that I have injuries to my ribs; two are broken and three have hairline cracks. My nose is also broken as is my right cheekbone. In addition to these injuries, I have many cuts on my arms from the broken glass. The doctor who initially examined me informs me that I shall be kept in the hospital.

While my ribs will heal with time, they are concerned about a possible internal haemorrhage.

All the time I am being examined and having the X-rays done, Shirley sits patiently in the waiting area; and when I ask a nurse to inform her that I am being admitted to the hospital, she offers to go to my home to inform my family. She is taken aback when I say I have no family in the UK and offers to stay with me awhile. All this time she has called me by my name: Deji.

Over the next few days she is the person who puts in a call to my university and the station on Monday to tell them that I will be off work for some time due to my injuries. Every day during visiting hours, she is here with flowers or chocolates or magazines. I think of all the animosity I have felt towards her over the last few months and regret my curt attitude.

On Monday evening, I see a familiar figure make his way towards my bed in the ward. It is Pete. I see the horrified look on his face as he takes in my swollen face and panda eyes, and I want to laugh out loud but I am restrained by my bandaged ribs from doing so. I have seen myself in Shirley's mirror and I dare say I look much worse than I am feeling today. Sure, the aches and pains are still here, but I resemble something that was salvaged from under an articulated lorry and barely snatched from the jaws of death.

I am pleased to see him and we fall into bantering in no time. He fills me in on the day's activities both at school and work. Less than an hour later, Shirley joins us and, too soon, visiting hours are up. I thank them both for visiting, and apologise to Pete for my rudeness the previous week. He brushes this aside.

I am in the hospital for a total of six days. Both Shirley and Pete are regular visitors at my bedside. On Thursday evening when I am discharged, it is Pete who comes to the hospital with his car to drive me home. Shirley is at the hospital with me by the time Pete arrives. When the nurses bring a wheelchair to transport me outside – not that I really need it – she insists on wheeling me to the car park, leaving Pete to trail alongside with the holdall that contains the few belongings I have amassed over my hospital stay. As we make our way down in the lift, Shirley tells an outrageous joke causing Pete and I to guffaw with laughter. My ribs still ache but I feel light-hearted. Beaming up at both of them from my position in the wheelchair, I think: 'It's good to have friends you can count on.'

Two Years to Grow Up

Rebecca Brianne Lever

USA/University of St Andrews

Here I am, sitting in the conservatory, watching a rain cloud get angrier, and waiting for the rain. I am alone in the house I share with two other students who have already gone home for the summer. I am contemplating the two years we spent together.

Last year, I moved to Scotland as a first-year student at the University of St Andrews. My parents flew out with me to help me move into hall. When May, my roommate, arrived, I was bustling about our room, trying not to appear like I was from po-dump-nowhere USA, and was determined to be best friends with this new person I was going to spend a year living with. We shared an initial glance that my parents would later describe as 'a sigh of relief in finding each other *normal*'. Our parents left us and we unpacked some more. I asked if she wanted the desk with the sea view, because I knew I wanted the one facing the wall. Rarely has something caught my attention like the beauty of the sea, and I knew that having something that interesting just beyond my computer screen would not be conducive to me doing any work.

May asked if I was sure, since she was quite happy to have the desk facing the wall, but I insisted. I knew that I wanted to prioritise my studies. As May continued unpacking she pulled out a pair of riding boots and a helmet. I was instantly excited. I had planned on continuing riding at university and was ecstatic that maybe we would already have something to do together besides share a sleeping space.

After our first dinner in hall we went down to the common room for a talk from our hall warden. He seemed a bit grumpy, but we figured we wouldn't bother him and he wouldn't bother us. One of the girls in the room next to ours had brought cake and champagne for all the girls on our floor, so we went in for a chat. I was too scared to try the champagne (having never had a drink in my life) and went for some cake. I learned that May had spent the past six months helping in an orphanage in Sri Lanka, and my admiration for her grew. She seemed so worldly and kind and, in a way, perfect. I was rather jealous.

It turned out she also was a Christian. I was from a small town in the south of the US, so I was surprised to find such a conservative attitude this far from home. However, I have spent my whole life around conservative Christians and was looking forward to the opportunity to have some good theological debates.

That first night the pair of us were tied together by the knees and sent off on a three-legged pub-crawl. May had to order for me since I had no idea what to order, having never been in a pub before. We sat in the pub and chatted with people in our hall and had our drinks. At our last pub stop, we chatted to the remaining people from our original group and made some more friends.

The next morning May went off to church and I met my parents for a walk and lunch. In the afternoon May and I planned out our freshers' week and we worked on decorating our room. During our freshers' week, we went to lectures on how not to plagiarise, started playing Ultimate Frisbee, signed up for classes, and started to bridge the language gap between us (how was I supposed to know that 'pants' no longer would include my jeans?). Even to this day, May bursts into fits of hysterical laughter at some of the very American things I say. Although I did attend a meeting for international students in freshers' week, the speaker didn't cover too many of the translations, except mentioning that we should never, ever ask for a fanny pack.

First semester flew by. I spent many Tuesday nights out at the St Andrews disco commonly referred to as the Bop. Occasionally May came along too, but mainly it was the rest of my friends collectively known as the A-Floor Girls (because most of us lived on the A-Floor of Sallies). We would make up themes for the Bop and dress up as zebras, superheroes, sailors, the Scottish flag etc. We loved dancing the night away and would pull out the most wacky and corny dance moves we could make up. It was there, surrounded by close friends and dancing the night away, that I knew I had come to the right university.

Near the end of first semester, May and I decided that we wanted to live together for our second year, and we asked our friend Grant if he wanted to live with us. I found us a house, and we signed the lease.

I didn't know Grant that well, but I figured that he couldn't be bad if he was a friend of May's. During our revision week in January, Grant ended up studying every day in our room, which indicated to me that we were going to have a good house – if we could all stress and study together and still have good times.

Onwards came second semester, and with it May's birthday. We had always joked that she could out-drink Grant, but we never really put her 'talent' to the test. One of the A-Floor girls took over the task of keeping May's glass full, and, boy, was it a night! May and Alison, one of her closest friends, both went maybe a bit over their own limits, but before that, all of us played silly games for hours, to the amusement of the Sallies Porter. I thought it was a great evening and a fun way to celebrate May's birthday, even if she was a little ill.

The following month was my birthday. I had planned a day of fun and games followed by a barbecue on the beach. In one of the earlier activities of the day, May, one of my guy friends and I went on a photo-scavenger hunt and went all out for our photos. I was so glad to have May as one of my friends. She always seemed to be verging on crazy. She was wild and fun. I knew that we never stayed up late sharing secrets, but I just ignored this fact and was happy to go on with our usual patterns.

It was near the end of the year when I learned one of the first real things about May. We were getting dressed in the morning, and I glanced up at May to ask her a question when I noticed a strange pattern of scars on her upper thigh, so I asked her about them.

I asked what had happened to her. She gave me a look that I would never forget. It was fleeting, but very dark. Her voice cracked as she answered me:

'I–I did that myself.'

I was stunned into silence. My wonderful, beautiful, friend May, doing what to herself? How long? Why hadn't I known? Was there something I could do? She assured me that she had stopped and was doing better. I wasn't convinced, but I asked her about it. And she told me about being on the edge, why she hadn't been able to go through with it.

Near the end of exams I had a conversation with Grant. It was pretty close to a heart-to-heart, although he's not really one for the good chat. He mentioned that we needed to make sure that May ate right. I was a little confused. Apparently she also had an eating problem, but I wasn't going to let that be a problem. I was determined that we were going to have a happy house.

Over the summer, I heard from May and Grant a few times, but for the most part I was back to small-town summer life. I worked at a little shop and planned to chill out with some friends.

By the time second year started, I was more than ready to get back to fun university life. So off I went, and I threw myself into everything I could. I played sports, took dance classes, went out with friends, spent hours in the library studying, and filled every second I could. It turned out that the three of us made for a busy house. Grant was out most evenings in meetings with his outdoor social groups and May would attend Christian meetings or work on her dance-class plans. I was usually the first out the door in the morning and last in during the evening, so there would be days when I wouldn't see May, and I would only see Grant during our lecture together. However, when the weekends rolled around, I got to spend lots of time with May and we would bake, take care of the house and enjoy each other's company.

After a couple of months into the semester, out came another of May's secrets. It turned out that May was actually dating our friend Alison. It also turned out that Grant had known about it for ages. I wasn't really offended. I mean, as far as I know, the best person that one can be for someone who is troubled is to be constant and someone who brings joy into their lives without forcing them to be someone they are not. If May didn't want to run to me with her problems (and joys, in the case of Alison), I understood. She had to decide whom to talk to about her problems. I was a little jealous that Grant was the one May had always run to when something was wrong, but I knew that if I mentioned it, she would feel obligated, and I definitely didn't want to force confidences from her.

For the most part, I was very happy; May had found love in the person who had been her best friend in the past year. But of course, it was a big secret. May could not tell her family, for fear of being disinherited and cut off, as had happened to her gay cousin, and she could not tell most of her university friends for several reasons. The main reason was that most of her friends were also Christian, and she feared that they would abandon her, in a similar manner as many of her friends did in high school. I told her that being truly herself was the only way to determine who her real friends were. She agreed, but I think we both knew that her letting that truth out was a long way off.

The semester kept pressing on, and I was busy but made efforts to keep our 'family' (as we referred to ourselves) still doing activities together. We always had Tuesday-night dinners in the house together like a proper family might. It quickly became one of my favourite family traditions. Sadly, along with an eating disorder, my dear May also suffered from depression. Before Christmas, she talked to me about going on some medication to treat it. I was instantly concerned. I knew that such medication potentially could be especially harmful to those who are younger, as in the case of a friend's boyfriend who committed suicide over the summer. I also knew that the adjustment time to such medication could be long, and I didn't think that the beginning of a semester was a good time to start adjusting to new drugs. She took them anyway.

While May was away over the break after exams, I expressed these concerns to Grant. He looked at me and said, 'Yes, but without them, May might no longer be with us.'

Like most families, we all wanted what's best for each other, even if we didn't know what that might be. I had to be patient, and hope for the best, even if that wasn't what I wanted to do.

Second semester started, and May was doing well. Well, for the first few weeks. I breathed a small sigh of relief. Maybe the medicine was actually working. Maybe she was getting better. It turned out that that was not so much the case. May was taking care of a friend of hers, Becky. May and Becky knew each other through Christian worship meetings held in Becky's hall. Becky's boyfriend had dumped her, because she was too needy and wanted to physically do too much. He felt that they were acting irresponsibly for Christians. Becky came crying to May and she spent two nights sleeping on our couch. I felt a little uncomfortable, mainly because there was something about her I just didn't like. I tried to like her, honest, but I felt as though her time spent in our home was strange. She ate in hall; she went to class; she did her schoolwork in our living room. She was living her normal life, except in my house. Why did she need May to get through her relationship issues?

After she moved out, for the next week or so she would occasionally come around for chats with May. After she left one night, I looked at May and said, 'I think your relationship with Becky is strange.'

'What do you mean?'

I didn't want to let on that I didn't like Becky, because who was I to deny May a friend, but I still had to say something, so I said, 'Well, it seems that she comes running to you with her problems, and she seems quite keen on calling you a friend, but you don't actually tell her anything about yourself. She doesn't actually know that much about you.'

'I know, but I like being able to help other people with their problems.'

Hmm, I thought to myself. It was funny that she knew and was happy with the situation.

After Becky sorted herself out and was a little happier with life, May crashed. She had a proper 'down' week.

May said to me: 'Becky doesn't come by anymore, because she is happy. She no longer needs me. I want to be part of her happy life too!'

I gave her a hug and thought to myself that I was there for a happy part of her life. I gritted my teeth though, and told myself that being pushy and needy was not exactly mature. I was going to be good, for May and my family.

Later on in the semester, when I was running around St Andrews doing errands, I ran into something that shocked me into anger. May was walking around in tears. I gave her the biggest hug and asked what was wrong, while thinking, 'Who on earth would hurt my May?'

She told me that Becky and she had a falling out, and that she had to go 'make things right' since they wouldn't see each other for two weeks. She wouldn't say anything more, but she went up to see Becky. I was confused and a little hurt by that non-explanation, but I had to trust that patience and time would be the right course of action. Why was May really walking around town in tears? Was something wrong with the world?

That night, when I got home, May was already asleep, but I caught Grant on his way to bed. I had to know what was going on – and if anyone would know what was going on, it would be Grant. I simply asked him about the strange occurrence I had witnessed earlier in the day: May in town, in tears. He sighed and told me to sit down, this was a long story. I snuggled up on the couch and waited for the epic.

The basic story was that the three of them had gone

for coffee that afternoon. A couple of days previously, May had told Becky that, actually, her ex-boyfriend had a bit of a point. May felt used and said that Becky was only really treating her own emotional needs. At this point I sucked my teeth, being pretty sure that this was May's greatest idea. It turned out that during coffee, Becky decided to have it out with May. Apparently May had taken on Becky's problems without it being her place, among other things. May walked out of Costa in tears, and Grant had remained and let Becky have her ramble, without really listening.

Our conversation continued for a long while, my first real heart-to-heart with Grant, which ended up in a long hug, me in tears, telling him how much he and May meant to me. We were, after all, family, and I loved them.

After finishing the last exam of my second year, I spent time with May and Grant relaxing here in the conservatory. One day, May and I sent Grant to the toilet, so we could have a girl chat.

May asked me, 'Do you,' and mouthed, 'wank?' with a gesture to her genital area.

I made a face and said, 'No, err, do you?'

'No, but I was just wondering . . . do you think that a lot of people do?'

I wasn't sure. I didn't think that it was really a topic of conversation.

Grant then walked into the room.

May gave me a pointed look, and said, 'Do boys do it?'

I snorted and said, 'Yeah, of course. I mean, Grant probably doesn't, but lots of guys do.'

'Really?' Grant wanted to know what we were discussing, since he was now involved.

I didn't want Grant to know what we were talking about – it was embarrassing.

Grant walked out with eyebrows raised.

May then asked me, 'How far down does the hairline go? I mean doesn't that hurt?'

I gave her a funny look, and said, 'I don't think that matters.'

'What do you mean?'

I laughed and said, 'I don't think we're talking about the same thing. What are you talking about?'

May said, 'What are *you* talking about?'

And I meekly said, 'Wanking.'

She had been talking about waxing down under! The pair of us sat laughing until we were crying with laughter.

I love the easy manner our friendship takes, like we're sisters. In one of our last chats of the year, May looked at me and remarked that lately she had been coming to me to talk about her problems and that Grant was a little upset and worried that he had done something wrong. I chuckled to myself and said, 'I know how he feels, but he can't take it personally. I didn't.'

Thinking back, I was right. I had spent two years wanting and waiting to be her best friend and ended up being more like family, and actually, I was happy with that. Maybe I couldn't always be the one she wanted to run to, but I learned to accept my role in each of their lives. I also began to recognise the good times, and I think, maybe, I grew up a bit.

Ceylonese Tea in the United Kingdom

Meleika Gooneratne

Sri Lanka/St George's, University of London

'Where are you from?'

A classic fresher question. In the top three along with 'What A level subjects did you do?' and 'What course will you be studying here?'

My reply of 'Sri Lanka. And where are you from?' usually elicited one of two reactions. Either people would have expected as much from my foreign accent or they would not have picked up on it at all, and startled, mumble that they were just from Darlington or Watford or Dagenham, and clearly had not expected me to come from quite so far away.

I swiftly realised that I was just a little bit unusual. I did not go home on weekends. I phoned my parents at weird Greenwich Meridian times to make sure that they were not asleep when I called. I did not drive up to college with my parents on the first day of university with my most-favourite-duvet-that-I-could-never-ever-possibly-live-without and the giant teddy bear that my (non-existent) sixth-form boyfriend had gifted me in the hope that I would never forget him. There just isn't enough luggage space for international students to fit the teddy in the overhead locker, and the kitchen sink was not within the 20 kg baggage limit.

No, our suitcases were packed with that ever-useful rice-cooker, because apparently British people do not know the secret of making good rice (the secret? Afore-mentioned rice-cooker), and an array of spices that were likely to be more potent than the devices metal detectors screened passengers for.

At least my mum got to come and see me off. I felt sad when she dropped me at the halls of residence, having travelled with me by coach all the way from Heathrow, and she cried, and I think all mums do that, whatever their nationality. The difference between me and a home student was that I knew it would be a year before I saw her again.

But in my first year I was not as homesick as some of my British friends. The UK was a complete novelty. I had never experienced such cold weather! I had never seen snow in my life and it is true what they say about brown people jumping around like mad 'uns in snow. Noël Coward wrote about mad dogs and Englishmen going out in the midday sun, but someone should probably sing a song about mad Asians dancing in the midnight snow. That was when I had my first lesson in frostbite and learned of the essentiality of gloves when handling snowballs.

I also learned in my first autumn that wearing shorts and flip-flops in the absence of the sun would shock all Brits (except for those from Cornwall, for some reason). 'You'll learn,' a British friend said sagely. In fact, I had trouble working out how many clothes to wear at all. I would bundle myself in so many layers that I looked like a big ball of wool on legs most of the time, and I still could not get warm.

But I loved it really. Hedgerows, sheep and oilseed rape fascinated me because we had learned about them in O level Geography. I was ecstatic the first time I saw an apple tree, much to the bemusement of my British peers. Living in a country where it was no issue for a girl to walk the streets in trousers, or in a skirt above the ankles, awed me. New experiences included buying my first pair of boots (the cheapest I could find, because anything above £5 seemed obscenely expensive to me) and wearing a coat for the first time. Scones and clotted cream were things I had only previously read about – mainly in Enid Blyton's books that now seemed more popular outside the UK than in it. So much had come to life for me.

I remember living on biscuits in my first term because I was too scared to spend money on myself. I think I put on the famous 'Freshers' 5 lbs' yearly weight gain in a week. At the end of my first year I had gained nearly two stone. When I returned home that summer, I was devastated because Sri Lankans are uncommonly blunt with their opinions and I was frequently greeted by, 'My, you've put on a lot, no?' Even the security guard at our block of flats cheerfully welcomed me back in Sinhala with, '*Hari mahatai ne!*' ('You've become very fat!'). I cried to my mum who reassured me that this was a compliment because in the villages they all aspired to become fat, and being fat was a sign of being well fed and wealthy. I was not convinced.

I think many international students go through similar food-related culture shocks in their first year. 'Luxury items' back home were widely accessible here. The first McDonalds in Sri Lanka was only established ten years ago. A Maccy Ds was a treat. £3 or (approximately) 500 rupees for a burger was extortionate – you could get four rice-and-curry packets for that! Only the affluent could afford pizza and KFC takeaways. In the UK it was the opposite. I could not get my head around the massive price differences in food, clothes and social costs. I found it incredibly hard to justify going on a night out, even though it was a very ingrained part of British culture.

Ah, and the first time I played the drinking game 'I have never'. Boy, I had never felt so backward and inexperienced in my life! For a girl who had never been kissed at the grand old age of eighteen and had never gone further than holding hands with a boy (and even then, just the one time because the giggling teenage girls in my class demanded so), I felt ashamed when my newfound friends were drinking to having had sex in a spaceship or some other adventurous, bordering-on-the-unbelievable exploit. I felt some catching up was in order.

But it was still many years and many mistakes later before I discovered true love, and meanwhile I was developing another love . . . for chocolate. Despite being female, I had honestly borne no affinity to it before coming to the UK. Sri Lanka was far too hot to enjoy chocolate. It was too hot and melty and sticky and a cold *thambili* (fresh juice from a king coconut chopped right in front of you with a straw inserted into the fruit) was far more refreshing. However, that soon changed as chocolate became my key source of fuel during my first ever winter.

It was to be my first Christmas in a foreign country away from family and home. I was a little bit daunted by the prospect of spending it as an adult pacing the empty college halls. It was then I discovered how false the old stereotype of 'cold Englishman' was, and how warm and kind-hearted British people could be. Three friends, including my college mum, invited me to their families' homes for Christmas immediately upon hearing my plight. I was incredibly touched. I ended up spending bits of my Christmas holiday with all three families and learned how hospitable and wonderfully generous people were. I look back fondly on gossiping under the covers with my English sisters late into the night, meeting their extended families and experiencing turkey and cranberry sauce instead of Christmas Curry – the Sri Lankan twist on Christmas that essentially involved adding raisins to everything and dying the rice yellow and pink. I enjoy my Sri Lankan Christmases very much, but it was lovely to experience an Anglo Christmas.

After that Christmas, I discovered I had been to more places in the UK than some Brits themselves. I did not want to be one of those people who never left the premises of their university. Coming all the way across oceans, it seemed daft not to explore the country. Places like Glasgow and Birmingham were of exotic and touristic interest to me, to the amusement of my friends. There was something enchanting about those little market squares and cobbled pavements, those big bridges and enormous ships docked at the harbours. I would always remember one of my friends exclaiming, 'You've never had a Cornish pasty before?' and our promptly sitting down on a bench in Weymouth with my first ever Cornish pasty – hot-and-filling stodge warming my insides against the icy wind. Coincidentally, I bumped into my old school principal, who is British, in Weymouth as he was there for his daughter's wedding, and he must have been surprised to find his little Lankan student had made it to Weymouth, of all places.

I joined a hill-walking club at university in the hope that it would be a good way to explore the UK with company and get some fresh air at the same time. We went to Snowdonia over Easter. I suppose it was common sense to everyone else, but I did not realise we were to bring sleeping bags. Coming from a trop-ical island where camping, mud and mountains were not really common features of growing up, I had no warning of how cold it would get. We were to stay in a twelve-bed cottage, dormitory style, and were told to bring our own sheets, but I had not realised they would not provide duvets nor, indeed, warmth. Too embarrassed to 'fess up once I had realised my error, I went to bed last, after everyone else had nodded off, wore every single item of clothing that I had with me and wrapped myself up in the thin linen sheets I had brought. I shivered so much that night I did not sleep a wink.

Meanwhile, I still had no luck on the romantic front, despite my desperation to catch up with my peers. Perhaps it was the fact that the desperate glint in my eyes actually set off warning bells in boys' heads sounding, 'Run! Run!' Perhaps I was too young and inexperienced and did not know how to 'play the game'. I felt decidedly unattractive and concerned that if, while I was supposedly at the peak of my life, I was not even being *flirted* with, this might be the end of the line for me. It did not help that, in conversation, quite a lot went over my head. I found it immensely hard to contribute to some conversations. I had not yet jumped on the *Neighbours* bandwagon, and was only just finding out that there was a place called the 'East End', let alone know that there was a soap on the people living there. Why on earth was this Jade Goody lady famous, and who is Katie Price and why is she now called Jordan/no, Katie Price/no, Jordan/ no, Katie?

I picked up a lot of new words in my first year. I learned when to use words and when not to. And I often had to find out the hard way. You see, I did not actually know what some of those words meant. All I gathered was that they were semi-rude, and I used many of them very inappropriately and out of context. One of the more innocent lapses in 'proper English' happened when I added the very commonly used 'Singlish' (Sri Lankan English) phrase 'isn't it?' after every sentence. I did not realise how close it was to 'innit' and was gently corrected by a Harley Street doctor's son, possibly at the point when his ears wanted to implode at my unacceptably poor grammar.

Another life lesson I learned, also the hard way, was how much to spend on gifts for people. It was a friend's birthday, and I asked another friend if she would not mind disclosing how much she would usually spend on a birthday gift. Unfortunately I decided to extrapolate because this was a very, very good friend. Ooh, my friends got such expensive gifts in my first year! And like a plummeting graph, how progressively stingier my gifts became! I could not make ends meet. I was ludicrously naive and had no financial acumen whatsoever, but I wanted to be generous. In my first term I took up a part-time job, as a waitress/bartender at a curry house. I am very glad I did it and it taught me many things and helped me to secure future part-time jobs, but I do hope never to return.

Over the winter my skin grew gradually paler. I used to be a rich cocoa brown but one winter later I looked more like weak Ceylonese tea. By Asian standards, this was great. Asians commonly have an almost Elizabethan complex that 'fairer is better'. The fairer the skin of a person, the more beautiful they were and their fairness insinuated a higher level of success and prestige. I guess this mentality arose from labourers having to work in the sun and becoming darker-skinned, whereas more privileged people could stay indoors and never saw the light of day, hence were fair-skinned (well, as much as an Asian could get anyway. It was never going to be a peaches-and-cream complexion now, was it?). The grass was always greener on the other side though, and I was constantly bemused by Caucasians lying on the grass with a bottle of suntan lotion at the slightest hint of sunshine. What really changed my thinking forever was my first ever Afro-Caribbean friend who went on a beach trip with me. She immediately stripped to the barest bikini and the coolest shades as soon as we touched sand. She then lay worshipping the sun, while I hid under a big hat and a baggy T-shirt, lathered in sun-cream factor +170. She could not understand it. 'Us dark-skinned people should relish our skin,' she explained, and went on to point out that skin tones look much richer once they are sun-kissed. I have never looked back, to the dismay of my parents. Here comes the sun, and here comes my picnic rug.

On the subject of skin, I did find true love eventually. Fortunately my parents are wonderfully open-minded by Asian standards and I knew it would never be an issue with them bringing a white boy back home. I think they half-expected it – me being someone who had always been a real struggle to manage, who was always challenging rules and tradition. He fell in love with my hot, soft brown skin and I fell in love with his cool, smooth, milky-whiteness. There is definitely some basis for the ancient Greek and Roman philosophy of Humorism where, through various extensions by Aristotle, Hippocrates and Plato, the hot and dry choleric male is inevitably drawn to the cold and moist phlegmatic woman, although I choose to believe the temperatures and temperaments are interchangeable.

It was a period of discovering 'ginger' too. Interestingly, I never thought twice about the fact that he was a redhead. I just thought he looked cute, as he earnestly engaged in intellectual conversation with one of my Lankan university friends on Sri Lankan politics, while I sat quietly gormless and occupied myself with surreptitiously edging away the vase of flowers between us so I could get a better view of his face. I later learned about how much stick gingers get, 'in good humour', and still hear awful comments from people saying how they would never date a ginger. Their loss! I am so glad I did not grow up with that particular prejudice.

Ultimately, living or studying in a foreign country boils down to learning how to assimilate into society, while retaining most aspects of your own culture. Throughout my university life, I have picked up more and more English vocabulary, occasionally pronouncing words with a British accent, because that is how I have heard them said, and my Lankan friends tease me about these occasional British interjections to my accent. I sometimes feel very mixed-up and this could be extended to a feeling of not quite belonging any-where. But who wants to belong to just one place? The world is huge, and I definitely feel a part of it, if perhaps an odd, slightly anomalous but unique addi-tion to a small subset of its population. And that makes me the luckiest person in the world.

Now if only I can figure out which international cricket team to root for!

Polar Bear

Eric Kalunga

Tanzania/Durham University

That cold morning the sky was grey. About thirty students filled the seminar room. Jonathan sat at the back.

The seminar leader, a kindly looking woman, smiled. 'Right, we shall start by getting to know one another. So move around and ask people what animal they would like to be and if they could go anywhere in the world where that would be.' She clapped her hands. 'OK, off you go!'

This was an ice-breaking exercise on the first day of a new module. There were sounds of chairs scraping the floor as people got up and the hum of several conversations descended upon the room. Here and there could be heard the occasional laugh.

'Hi, I don't think I have spoken to you yet?' she said.

Jonathan, who had just been speaking to a girl from Taiwan, shook his head and smiled. 'No. Hi.'

The woman extended her hand, 'I'm Sharon.'

'Jonathan.'

She nodded, 'Mmnh, what a nice, strong Englishman name.'

And that was when Jonathan began to feel ashamed of his name. The rest of the conversation went right over his head. Eventually she moved on and Jonathan slumped back into his seat, not sure anymore that he wanted to meet anyone else. He thought of Ngugi Wa Thiong'o, the Kenyan writer who had renounced his name James because it was English and so colonialist.

'Hello, I am Yasmin, from Palestine,' said another girl. She had long black hair and an alluring smile.

For the moment at least Jonathan forgot his conflicted emotions. 'Hi, I'm Jonathan, from Tanzania.'

They smiled for a second or two then she produced a pen and paper and asked the next question. 'OK, so if you were an animal; which one would you be?'

The pen hovered over the paper as she waited.

'A polar bear. You?' asked Jonathan.

'A butterfly.' She frowned. 'So, are there polar bears in Tanzania?'

'No.' In his mind flashed an image of a polar bear, snout dripping with blood, fur tainted red, standing over the bloody carcass of a seal. It was on the *National Geographic* channel. 'But I think they are, they are strong and fearless . . .' he trailed off.

She nodded.

He thought of changing his answer to a lion. There were plenty of those in Tanzania. 'So are you doing a PhD?' he asked instead.

After lunch he sat with his laptop. He was poked on Facebook by his girlfriend. He poked her back. It was their little game. Fun at first but now it was getting tiresome.

'I just love poking you,' he wrote and posted that on her wall.

There were some friend requests, none of them exciting. He left them there. Then he navigated to Kadshah's page, a girl he met on a student trip. She had posted pictures of flowers from a garden she had visited earlier. Several of her friends liked the post. 'Luvly!!!' posted one. He clicked on the tiny thumb-up sign and liked her post. Then he sent her mail asking her to meet for coffee. Jonathan had shared a seat with Kadshah on the coach from Newcastle when they went on an international student trip. They had agreed to meet sometime for coffee.

Now they were sitting at the college bar.

'How was class?' he asked. He wondered how nice it must be to have a name like Kadshah, a name that no one could hold against you.

She said it was fine and told him a little about it. They spent a few minutes talking lectures and then giggled about students from China and their English. Then she began fumbling inside her bag.

His phone tweeted. He read the text.

'I have to go.'

'I have to go.'

They both spoke at the same time.

She smiled. 'Oh, where are you going?'

'The Lion.'

'Oh, OK, catch you later.' She got up and left.

Married, he thought as he got up and left too. Night had already fallen when he finally arrived at the pub, The Black Lion. On one table sat John, a PhD student from Cameroon, and Ekpechi who was from Nigeria.

He went to the counter to get his drink and then joined them.

'This is the first time that I feel like an African,' Jonathan said as soon as he sat down. He sipped his Morgan's Spiced double shots. On one wall was mounted a plasma screen, a Sky Sports presenter was talking while below him scrolled text of the latest scores. They couldn't hear the presenter over the loud pop music that was playing.

'I am not just Jonathan anymore, I am a black person and an African and a Christian and I feel weird about it,' Jonathan went on.

His friends remained silent.

'And it feels like every time the lecturer is talking about Africa it is poverty and Aids. I feel like I have to protest but—'

'This again,' John muttered. 'Listen, you just write your exams and pass.' He lifted his lager mug to his mouth before realising it was empty.

'What does it mean?'

'What does what mean?' John asked.

Jonathan nodded towards Ekpechi. 'His name.'

John sighed, picked up the empty mug and stood. 'Anyone want a refill?'

The other two shook their heads. John disappeared in the direction of the counter.

'I don't really know. I think it means praying to God and saying thanks,' Ekpechi said. He sucked on the straw that jutted from his Coke.

'That's great. So it's Christian but still African.'

'The two aren't mutually exclusive.'

John came back with a filled mug. 'Do you know

that girl? She keeps looking at you.'

On a dark corner of the bar sat two girls. One had dark hair and the other one was a blonde.

He shook his head. 'No.'

'She is fine,' Ekpechi said.

Jonathan nodded. At this time the blonde girl looked in their direction and then quickly turned away.

'The two aren't mutually exclusive at all,' Ekpechi went on.

'That's true especially for you. Maybe this is something you never had to think about. You have your African name and are a Christian too,' Jonathan said.

John sighed. 'It isn't hard to tell that this is your first time abroad.'

Jonathan shrugged.

'These are things I dealt with a long time ago,' John went on. He pointed at his own chest as he leaned across the table to stare at the other two. 'My name is John Adam. Do you know how that sounds on paper? White. Guess what happens when someone finally sees my picture or I appear in person.' He leaned back in his seat and sipped his beer.

'That's just rubbish,' Ekpechi waved his hand dismissively. 'How can you know that someone is being racist and not just liking you because you are a man or they had a bad day or because your mouth stinks?'

'They are all racist,' John snarled.

The two girls at the corner were now joined by three boys, two white and one black. They seemed to be having fun.

'Guys, see you later.' Jonathan left and walked home.

That night Jonathan was surprised to learn that one

of his housemates had eight children. Jane, the house-mate, was very thin and wore jeans and sweaters. Also one of her children was called Nina Ricci, after the perfume.

'I have been talking to people from other countries on Facebook and all their names seem to mean something.'

They were standing in the kitchen, the one place where the housemates occasionally got to meet during the day. She was waiting for her chilli-beef lasagne in the microwave while his chicken curry and rice was waiting on the slightly greasy countertop.

'What about Jane?' he asked.

She shook her head and wrapped her hands around her chest. 'My aunt was called Jane. That's all.'

Jonathan nodded. 'Well, it's yours now and you can do what you want with it.'

She smiled. The microwave pinged. She opened the door and got out the steaming dish. The smell of beef wafted out.

'You can also name your children what you want,' said Jonathan. He got a fork and went about piercing the film lid on his curry and rice. A few fork stabs later he was satisfied and placed the dish into the micro-wave.

'My daughter is called Nina Ricci because I love the perfume,' she said.

'See, now she will know what her name means,' Jonathan said.

Jane nodded to herself. Then she picked up her plate and with a brief glance and another brief smile left the kitchen.

Jonathan was watching his food spin and get hot when Sean, the other housemate, walked into the kitchen. He was with a friend.

'You alright?' Sean said. 'Going out tonight?'

'Hi,' Jonathan responded. 'No, no money.'

'Hi, I'm Wendy,' said the girl.

'Hi. I am Jonathan, nice to meet you.'

They shook hands.

Shards

David Molloy

Australia/University of East Anglia

The fragments are skipping away. They run along synapses like squirrels in trees, evading me. I have to jog to keep up with many of them, while the others jostle for attention. There is a scrum in my head. A carnival set off by five simple words. In three months time, numerous friends and relatives will again set off this madness almost unthinkingly, and in their genuine curiosity will send me into frenzy. But they want to know, and I want to remember. So I squeeze my eyes and ponder how exactly to answer the question in a timely fashion, to keep the audience interested.

'So how was your trip?'

Good question.

Trying to place that old world within the geography of my skull is difficult. Those people I love are vividly remembered, distant in space but not in time. It's hard to imagine where I want to be more now, that country where I was raised and made so many wonderful friends, or this new and more challenging place. Displacement is a curious thing – dual nationality has the effect of splitting you down the middle and forcing you to choose which hemisphere you can do without for longest.

I sit here in Norwich, tapping away at the keyboard in her fingerless gloves, wishing she could return so I could set aside this mundane week. She's off having her own adventure across the seas, in the US, where I presume she's being shot at twenty-three hours a day.

As much as I'm aware, this person tapping is a very different one to the boy who stepped off flight BA10 onto the tarmac of Heathrow Airport on a cold New Year's Eve not so long ago. Logic denotes that the tale begins there, but the story is splintered, like a rhizome still growing within me.

Maybe it's better to begin with the young man playing in the snow. He is wearing layers of winter clothing bought in a country that has no understanding of this kind of cold. Despite this, he frolics in the powder, revelling in the wonder of it. He forms small spheres of it in his hands, stacks them together. Using pine-cones and twigs, a rudimentary personality is projected onto the pile. Click. A photo of his first tiny snowman sent home to the family. People three years his junior chuckle at his enthusiasm from elevated windows. They're too busy complaining about the weather to enjoy it. Alone, he laughs.

Rewind to the night before, dancing crazily with newfound friends as lasers fly around their heads. He memorises a piece of advice to give to the folks back home – drink with a Scotsman. After a few pints, *everything* will be on him. On the dance floor, she moves closer to him. The dance gets serious. The boy gets his first kiss on foreign soil. There are more to come.

Further back in time, and the boy stands before the London Eye, with Westminster sprawling around him. A single snowflake falls on his nose and sparks a rush of exultation through his entire body. He is truly living the dream. He is in another world.

Somewhere in between snow and snogging, I managed to unpack my stuff and debrief my week in London. I even attended classes. I was welcomed warmly into the halls of Norfolk Terrace by curious freshers. It was like reliving my first year. In a sense, it was my first year.

The boy is back. Ducking between trees in the woods. All the flatmates bar one have declined this brief sojourn around the Broads. He photographs *everything* – every twisted tree, every shard of light shattering the canopy. They swing from a rope tied to a tree in a clearing. They muse over the possibility of starting a bonfire here. They separate. Alone, he speeds into the undergrowth, eager to beat her home. Then suddenly he stops.

The dog stares at him, eyes curious. It stands questioningly, eyes locked with the boy. It turns and wanders away amongst the trees. The boy will not see it again.

His excursion into the forest proves an adequate training for the man, locked in fierce battle many months later. Clutching my rifle, I step cautiously over bracken and nettle. The elfish hollow of a Devon wood whispers around me. A rustle to my left. Breathe. Aim. My finger lingers on the trigger for only a moment. Then, BANG. The pellet strikes my foe in the centre of his forehead, causing him to call out a ceasefire. A sadistic grin crosses my face.

As we both stumble from the trees, we emerge on a river's edge, and she is in the water. The water curls invitingly around her stomach. She shivers slightly. Her smile is warm, and her laugh infectious. I haven't heard it in a while.

The boy meets her, too. Sitting opposite her in a screenwriting class. She is the only interesting person in the room. And *she* pursues *him*, to a degree. Eventually the boy works up the nerve to ask her out for drinks. She is far from coy the whole night. Cradling a gin and tonic, playing with a lock of her dyed-blonde hair, she rests her leg against his. The boy blushes inwardly. 'This is amazing,' he mumbles. 'Someone I'm attracted to that I can actually maintain conversation with.' They lean into each other and kiss with all the nervous energy of teenagers.

A week later they emerge as if from a reverie. They walk together to the bus stop. Her arm is wrapped around his waist. My waist. The man emerges.

Imago. The man's wings spread, eager for the sky. I adventure across the seas again. Germany, Scotland, Holland, Belgium, France, Italy, Spain. Europe opens up to me, a world of new experience, new sensations and new people. For the first time, I exist in a place where white, English-speaking, heterosexual males are not the dominant species. I struggle with fragments of language as numerous as pieces of memory. My Dutch friends, strangers I met on New Year's Eve, embrace me warmly and question my blue hair. They give me every Dutch foodstuff they can name. I consider the stories I'll have to tell to my friends after I stumble into a hostel room to find five Greek girls adorned in towels and nothing else. I wander in silence through the war memorials of Berlin. I dance while bursts of flame erupt overhead. I shiver in the harsh winds of Edinburgh. My pupils widen in Amsterdam. I stagger drunkenly across Antwerp after a night out with the locals. I fall in love with Bruges. I steal a kiss on the ceiling of the Cathedral de Notre Dame. I stare in tears of awe at the Colosseum.

Reunited, we dangle our feet over a castle wall, overlooking a vineyard in Tuscany. The smell of olive oil is on our skin, in the air. I hold her to me and try to conjure in my head some vague idea of what life was like before all of this. She kisses me, and none of it matters.

A month later, she holds me to her chest, my blood staining her shoulder. She is unable to visit when I am hospitalised after the assault. Her friends take me in and treat me as their kin, making me soup to compensate for the solid food I can't eat. They are hospitality in essence. Not one of them jokes about the attack, at least not until later. I try to smile but my fractured jaw protests, so I lie back, close my eyes and hope they know how grateful I am to them.

The jaw still hurts as I cavort amongst the masked. Beneath London Bridge, a crowd gathers around the feast table, where gold-painted nudes recline as centrepieces. I have a work of art painted on my chest. I wink to the girl in the centre of the table, who returns the gesture and strokes my face with a peacock feather.

The cheekbone still hurts as I mosh to Rage Against

The Machine, leaping through the crowd at Download. But it is less persistent now. Entrenched in mud, I make new friends, all of us united by a shared passion for music. We wave our arms as one to the sounds of Aerosmith.

I look at my profile photos as I write, trying to remember some of the people in them. So many different faces. So many of them are me, or were me, and maybe never will be again. Her warmth lingers as if she is touching my arm, and I long for her. It will be near impossible to leave this place, when so much has gone before me, and so much is waiting to happen. At home I know there are warm embraces waiting for me, hot meals and excited questions. Old friends and new acquaintances, old lovers and new, and all my family begging for the details.

And only pieces will float by in the tide, yet I'll snatch what I can from the water and give it speech. I will tell them that Belgian beer surpasses any other. I will tell them that Australians can be found in every single country in the world. I will tell them never to set foot in Walkabout. I will tell them how AC/DC spent the entire economy of a third-world country on their stage design. I will tell them about Ian McKellen in *Waiting For Godot*. I will tell them of the highly addictive game invented in Carlisle that involves hitting ping-pong balls at your friends. I will *never stop* talking about clotted cream. I will wax lyrical on the virtues of the Dutch, the amicability of the Scottish, the party-fever of the Germans, and the bi-polar manner in which the French alternate between kindness and blatant hostility.

And most of all, I will tell them about a girl whose hair changed colour from week to week. Whose body I helped paint gold for a masquerade. Who drinks gin like it's going out of style. And with whom I shared my life for the better part of a year.

They will tell me of the boy that left six months ago, and the man that stands before them now. They will laugh when I say 'half six' instead of 'half-past six', give me a ribbing when I mention 'pounds', and offer me tea and scones at all hours. They will joke about my accent. And all they'll ever understand is fragments, which is all I'll ever be able to give them.

I can only hope that one day, as I chase those pieces of myself, that they will lead me back to her, back to these shores. Back to my new home.

Stopping to Catch Snow on My Tongue

Lucille Valentine

South Africa/Northumbria University

During my first winter in Northumberland, I realised that the weather could actually kill me. I had gone running. It was a long lovely route, one that I had run before. Leaving the farm house where we lived I headed through the neighbouring farm, up a little hill between the cows on the left and some very cold-looking ponies on the right. When I did get to the main road I did not stay on it for long, I ducked right. Back into the Tyne Riverside Park where the ground between the massive old trees, all the muddy forest floor, was frozen hard underfoot. I thumped my way across the narrow metal bridge over the River Tyne, to Ovingham, threaded briefly between the old buildings, headed left, past the town's school and along the long, long road that took me alongside the River Tyne to the next bridge, and then the next town, Stocksfield. Only then did I turn in to complete the circle home, and get back onto farmland again.

I was not suitably dressed. I had thought that I would warm up, because that was what always happened.

Not this time. I should have worn a hat, gloves, vest and warm shoes; at minimum I should have worn pants that covered my legs.

The brain thinks that everything can be understood and be prepared for, that the memory that resides in the head is comprehensive, is sufficient for making projections from; the head thinks that it is in charge. Then this sort of thing happens. I under prepare, I under dress, because of body memory which is stronger than head imagining. My body memory had no experience of such unrelenting cold weather and therefore it did not believe the freeze existed. Then came the moment when, closing a sheep gate with its fluttering dirty brown wool, having come five miles and still a mile from anywhere, I was exhausted and alone on a public footpath with farm fields on all sides and no chance that anyone would be coming by. The snow started.

To my tired eyes it seemed that the snow did not fall from the sky; irregular ice tissue-paper floating, matrix like, had simply materialised around me. I was entranced. For a minute I slowed to a walk to play and catch snow on my tongue. And within that minute I was freezing. Bone cold. Scared cold.

I couldn't get myself running again, couldn't make my muscles work and thought, OK, I would walk home. But my teeth, my molars, were rattling onto one another and I heard an animal groan and growl, but realised that it was me, I was making the sounds. Because my body knew that resting, waiting, getting my breath back would be the death of me, I pushed on. Over the stiles, past the huddled bumps of cows, over the rabbit hill, and eventually arriving at the huge portcullis gate that would lead me onto the farmyard if I could only get it open.

Once home I had a deep hot bath, but I cried myself to sleep that night.

My body memory has tripped me up again and again. There was the day, just a few weeks after I came to the UK, when I was trying to buy oats, just break-fast oats, nothing fancy. I was at the Co-op in Prudhoe and had gone down onto my knees to study the boxes and bags of rolled oats, breakfast oats, Scots oats, organic oats, free-range oats, metric and imperial oats. I had been there so long that someone was leaning over me to get to the muesli. When I stood up I nearly knocked the elderly gentleman off his feet. As I would in South Africa, I said 'sorry' while also steadying him, lightly, briefly, clasping his arms above the elbow. The air around us both became frosty, the man turned to stone, his expression locked in place until I opened my hands and we disengaged. There was not enough oxygen left between us for me to apologise again.

Our biggest error was in our choice of house. What you don't know can confuse you. The house was exactly what I had thought I wanted. A stone cottage on a working farm, where shy bunny rabbits bounced their little white bums down the driveway on Easter Sunday morning. Within a few weeks the farmer had put up a careful, sweet sign that warned everyone coming onto the farm to 'Drive Carefully, Children Playing'. This was mainly because our two boys raced everywhere, over gravel hill and across cow field dale; they struck-up friendships with the ponies Star and Spot and were fascinated by the nameless horses and the care given by the owners who stabled on the farm.

We could walk to the River Tyne within five minutes and we were under hills and by fields that actually grew stuff. There was the enormous patch of canola that was knee high when we moved in and became head high, sickly sweet yellow flowers by summer, and there was silage, grown and harvested into huge black plastic-covered wheels before I actually realised that they were a crop.

Mostly the farm dealt in cows, or rather calves, because the farmer bred them for meat, not milk. Calving had already started when we arrived in March and the boys got to see them deal with a difficult birth, the ropes and pullies and metal encouragers that luckily resulted in a live, mucus-covered calf. When the calves were weaned, when they were separated from their cuddling, nuzzling mothers, they were penned up in the barn adjoining our house. This led to our most intensely bovine time. Over endless nights and days, the calves would call and the cows would respond; and the mooing and moaning kept us from our sleep because they were babies who wanted comfort and our bedroom was on the calf side of the house.

I started studying because I had the time, because I had been wanting to do a post-graduate writing course for ages, and because I wanted to get away from the house.

I was alone during the day. My husband went off to work before eight in the morning to catch the bus into the city, then the boys and I walked up the hill to school and I returned to the cold house. With its single glazing, massive stone walls and crucially, I later thought, the fact that it almost never got any sun, the house seemed to lose heat more quickly than the central heating could supply it and I was always cold when I was home in the day.

Six months after moving to the country, to the farm, I was going running as often as I could gather myself together, and preferably at midday. I wanted sunlight, or sun, but simply light would do. Light filtering through cloud, light dodging raindrops, light glinting off snowflakes. At the house, if the sun was at the perfect angle, the rays fell through the back door, warming a rectangle of linoleum. Sky gold. I would bring a straight-backed chair from the dining room and sit there with a book or some knitting, there where my view was of driveway gravel and an elderly garage. I edged the chair along as the light shifted. Until it was gone.

No other room, upstairs or downstairs, got any sun. The reason for this was so utterly and completely obvious, but I missed it. On the south side of the house, double the height of the house, was a massive huge great green-roofed barn that blocked all but midday, mid-summer sun from the house. I never thought about the sun as being something to think about. In South Africa in summer I had my favourite shady outdoor spots and my home was kept cool by shutting out the sun in the middle of the day. Winter was never around for long enough for me to completely believe that it was real; I would stick it out, hibernate in one way or another with warm drinks and fires, and soon warmth returned. Here in the North-East of England I would have to be more strategic.

My younger son came out of the local first school ten minutes before the older, which led me to spending at least twenty minutes in the bright school yard every day, and this was a highlight. I was depressed, low, down, blue, cold and homesick. My body memory clung to its own past. I was not able to keep the house clean. I could not bear to always having the lights on, though it seemed to me that I had to and, even then, nothing was particularly bright.

The cold hurt my back, my shoulders hunched up and my body held itself in, in, in.

When the snow came I tried driving. I gave up after a day of having the station wagon slide sideways when I wanted to go straight and then slipping downhill, moving toward the farm faster than the car's wheels were turning. If I couldn't walk it, I simply didn't go. In my grey house, at the bottom of the hill in the perpetual shade of the green barn, I plodded, I persevered, I paid with my body to learn the moods of the new country.

When our lease came up for renewal, we looked for another house to buy or to rent, anything, anywhere. We hunted online, we traipsed to Whitley Bay, to Wallsend, arriving late because of the snow; I viewed scud-bucket flats in Heaton, tiny perfect overpriced jewel flats, lovely forest-backed homes, ramshackle large upper flats, in any and every suburb of Gateshead and Newcastle upon Tyne. My husband and I looked and we compared notes. We made lists of requirements and debated the merits of every place he and I visited. One day in February he took a bus from work to view a rental property, a place that I had not seen, and when he came home that evening he said, 'I took it, I signed the lease.'

I gaped. We don't do that sort of thing. We agree, we confer, we collaborate. I asked him why, why did he sign the lease without talking to me first? He just shrugged. I asked him what he had liked about the place.

He smiled at me with innocent happiness. 'The sun was shining,' he said.

Puzzled

Zoé Perrenoud

Switzerland/Bangor University

September 2006. I had just turned nineteen in August and was about to start over in a completely new environment. For the first time in years, I would have a clean slate. No one would know me. I didn't have to be the bookworm sitting alone in a corner of the classroom, the girl who rarely went out partying and didn't have a boyfriend. I could be anything I wanted to be. As my mum and I loaded my stuff into her car, I felt a strange mix of fear and anticipation. What if I didn't make any friends? What if it was all too overwhelming and I didn't fit in? What if I didn't enjoy my course? I stared out at the passing countryside, trying to reason with myself. Of course I would love my course. I'd waited so long to do this.

'But what if they don't like what I write?' I asked my mum.

'I'm sure they will. Besides, everybody else in your class will be starting out too. You're all going there to learn.'

'What if I make silly mistakes?'

'Like what?'

'Spelling mistakes or something. I'm no good at writing essays . . .'

'That's what the teachers are there for. To help you improve.'

But what if they were horrified, I thought as I struggled with sea-sickness on the ferry crossing the Channel. I had never read a Shakespeare play in my entire life. I guessed I would be alright with the Creative Writing part of my course, the part I was most excited about. But what about English Literature? I barely knew my Brontë from my Austen, having studied only a handful of modern Anglophone texts in high school. My bookshelves at home were filled with fantasy novels which I was sure would never feature on any university reading list. I felt certain that quoting French authors like Flaubert and Zola wasn't going to get me anywhere. By the time we reached Bangor, my second choice out of the six UK universities I had applied to, I was a nervous wreck.

The next morning, after a night spent tossing and turning in a hotel bedroom, I went with my mum and stepfather (who was working in London and had caught the train up to join us) to the Ffriddoedd site, the largest halls complex at the University of Bangor. Some-where, in the scattering of tall pink buildings with rows and rows of identical windows, my room was waiting for me. After picking up the key from the halls office, we headed off to find my block, Y Glyder. There were several students standing around wearing bright yellow T-shirts, so I walked up to one and asked for directions.

'Excuse me, I'm looking for Y Glyder. Do you know where that is?'

'What's that?'

'Y Glyder.' I mumbled it, almost certain that I wasn't pronouncing it right.

'Elidir?'

Oh dear. It sounded as though some of the buildings had very similar names. Defeated, I showed the student the piece of paper I had been given.

'Oh, the T-block! That's just round the corner to your left and down at the end.'

I should have known there would be a simpler version. Luckily, I wasn't the only one struggling with the Welsh names surrounding us. I didn't know to what extent the locals used Welsh in their everyday lives. In fact, before applying to the University of Bangor, I'm ashamed to admit I had no idea that such a language even existed. During the journey to Bangor, I had learned that *araf* meant 'slow' and *llath* meant 'yard', as these words were peppered all over the Welsh roads and signposts, but that was the full extent of my vocabulary. Over the next few weeks, I would hear rumours of cleaning ladies insulting the non-speakers in front of them if the kitchens were left in a mess. Four years on, I can happily say that this has never happened to me and that our cleaning lady in that first year was extremely friendly and helpful.

Once I found my room and admired the architect's skill at cramming a toilet, sink and shower into about one square metre of bathroom, I ventured into the shared kitchen to claim some cupboards and a shelf in the fridge. Luckily, only two other students had arrived, so I was able to commandeer enough space for all my pots and pans. An enlightening visit to the supermarket reassured me that I would find food I liked – the presence of Lindor chocolates promising ample comfort in case I got too homesick. Then came the time for my parents to go back to their hotel. I knew we wouldn't be saying goodbye until the following day, but seeing them drive off made me feel a bit sad. I was almost on my own now. That evening, the peer guides (those students in yellow) would take us out for a night on the town. I would have to make contact and start telling others about myself.

It was a daunting prospect, but as I discovered later, I needn't have worried about it. Within ten minutes of leaving the Ffriddoedd site, I had found at least two other people who liked *Pirates of the Caribbean*. Someone knew about Hayao Miyazaki and Japanese Anime. Lots of them liked *Harry Potter*. Most of them were just as nervous as me, if not more. I found my fellow students surprisingly easy to talk to, with everyone eagerly asking questions. I felt, for the first time, that people really wanted to get to know me. It was a wonderful feeling, but at the same time it started to colour my memories of life in Switzerland. Were people there colder than I'd realised? I suddenly felt as though I'd spent the last few years surviving instead of living. I'd reached the happy point where my classmates accepted me and left me alone, but now I was discovering what it felt like to be fully integrated. To be a part of something. It filled me with exhilaration, but at the same time I feared I would lose some of the love I had for my home country.

'You'll be fine,' my mum said to me the following morning.

We hugged and I watched them drive away, a few tears prickling at the corners of my eyes. That afternoon, curled up in bed with the noises of students settling in above and to either side of my room, I wondered what I was doing there and who I would become.

Halfway through freshers' week, I entered the kitchen to find some of my flatmates sitting around the table, talking about their futures.

'So why did you choose Zoology?' asked Liz.

Jack was the one studying Zoology. He shrugged. 'I guess I like animals.'

'But what do you want to do after your degree?'

'I really don't know. I could be the village baker, for all I care. I'm just here for the experience.'

We all laughed and nodded and went our separate ways.

Long after the conversation was over, I couldn't shake off the worry it had planted inside my mind. I'd only just learnt about student loans and how almost every student seemed to have one. Whenever anyone asked if I had received mine yet, I would say something along the lines of 'It doesn't work the same for me.' As they all knew I came from a foreign country, they just assumed it was an international student thing. I didn't want to admit that my parents were the only ones helping me, because I was afraid of 'Swiss bank account' comments being thrown my way. As I've had to point out a few times, everyone living in Switzerland has a Swiss bank account. It's no more amazing than having one anywhere else. It certainly doesn't make you automatically rich.

'I'm going to end up with £15,000 of debt by the end of my studies,' a friend said to me, much later on.

It was a £15,000 experience and some of them didn't have a clue what they were going to do when it was over. I couldn't believe it. When the recession hit the UK two years later, I could hear the words 'national debt' ringing in my ears like the echo from a destructive blast. I thought of Switzerland, where only twenty percent of the population go on to study at university. Tuition fees are in the hundreds rather than the thousands. It is almost easier to get a job after an apprenticeship than after a three-year BA. In 2008, we all watched the British economy crash, but they carried on raising tuition fees, preparing to shoot themselves in the foot over and over again.

That first week, it almost seemed like I closed my eyes on the Monday and opened them again only to realise it was Friday. Everything went past in a blur, but the Saturday night still sticks out in my mind like a bright neon sign. I had been invited to a fancy-dress party by one of the peer guides, a girl named Anne. I've always loved to dress up. Back in high school, I once hired a proper eighteenth-century-style dress complete with hooped underskirts for what was called Extravagance Day. This time, my mind simply went blank at the idea of coming up with a decent costume, so I settled for a slightly dressy top and a pair of jeans. I was counting on the fact that every fancy-dress party usually has a few people who turn up in casual clothing.

Once inside Anne's living room (my first time in a proper house since the start of the week), I settled down to observe the different people there. One girl sitting on the couch opposite me gave me a flash of false hope (I was beginning to get a little homesick by now). She was wearing a red dress with tiny Swiss flags stuck in her hair. I lost no time in asking her where she was from, but she turned out to be German.

'What about the flags?' I asked, a tad disappointed.

'I'm supposed to be a cheese girl. Swiss cheese?'

I nodded, amused. It made sense, after all.

There were a lot of people at the party and they all seemed to know each other, so it took me a while and a couple of drinks to feel comfortable. At some point, a boy wearing an Arnold Schwarzenegger mask around his neck came and sat next to me. We started talking. His name was Tom. He was studying Modern Languages. Not only did he speak quite decent French, but he'd also lived in Switzerland when he was very young. He knew what I was talking about when I mentioned certain place names. He seemed really nice, but one thing about his appearance kept distracting me. On his neck, just above the collar of his shirt, was a big black patch, the size of a £2 coin. I found myself wondering what it was and whether I was sitting next to someone with some mysterious, incurable disease. The conversation turned to his costume.

'I got this on eBay,' Tom said, lifting the mask from around his neck and putting it on. 'Arnie's my favourite actor.'

He seemed a little embarrassed by this statement.

'That's interesting,' I replied, knowing that I would just have to accept a gaping difference in our cinematic tastes. I'm a Johnny Depp fan all the way.

'I got these bullet holes as well.'

It took me a moment to realise that he was pointing at the strange patch on his neck. I laughed.

'What?'

It was my turn to be embarrassed.

'I thought you had the plague or something.'

Luckily, he wasn't offended and I was ranting to my mum on the phone the next day about having made a new friend. Six weeks later, we became more than friends. Almost four years on, we are engaged to be married and living together, despite regular debates about the high points of Arnold Schwarzenegger's acting career. Tom has accepted that if I meet Johnny Depp, I am entitled to run away with him. Decidedly, Bangor is full of surprises.

After a short length of time, in that first year, the inevitable happened. I ran out of clothes.

Armed with my laundry basket and a book, I headed for the campus *golchdy*, as they call it in Welsh. Most of the machines were already taken, but I spotted a free one at the end of the room. When I opened the drawer to put the soap in, I discovered a thick layer of bright blue gunk clogging up the small compartment and had to back down in horror. Mixing powder and washing-up liquid was obviously not a good idea. Luckily, a couple of minutes later, another machine finished and I was able to place my clothes in a gunk-free zone. Then, thinking this was the normal thing to do, I sat down on one of the rickety plastic chairs and delved into my book (I would soon learn that no one ever waits for their washing in the laundrette. It is considered incredibly sad to do so).

Fifteen minutes later, a group of students walked in to check on their laundry. They were chatting amicably, but I could tell that they were all freshers by the questions they kept asking each other. I smiled and said hi, still marvelling at how easy it was to make contact with strangers here. One of the girls said hi back and came over to talk to me.

'Where are you from?' I asked after a couple of minutes.

The girl looked surprised, offended almost.

'Isn't it obvious?'

'Well, no. I'm not from the UK, so I don't know all the different accents.'

Her eyes went wide and I could tell I'd just narrowly saved myself from a very delicate situation.

'Oh, sorry. I'm from South Wales. Where are you from?'

'Switzerland.'

'Oh, right. Well your English is very good.'

'Thanks.'

Your English is very good. I've had that one a lot over the past four years. It's really nice, but then I tell them that my mother is British and it kind of ruins the myth. Sometimes, it turns into a bit of a game and I ask people to guess where I'm from. They usually say the south of England. That's not even close, as my grand-mother lives in Sheffield. Yorkshire born and bred as she would put it. It sometimes feels like I'm cheating when I say I'm foreign. At other times, I couldn't feel more different from the people surrounding me. It took me three years to even go near baked beans. Vinegar on chips is possibly one of the most revolting culinary concepts ever invented. People stare at me when I leave out the milk in my tea. I've discovered I can't play any board games like Cranium because I haven't got a clue about British TV presenters and all that lot. Still, I have found that being a bit different can be quite comforting at times.

Soon enough, once I had ditched any traces of shyness, I was partying the night away every Monday in Time, one of Bangor's three nightclubs. The theme was cheesy music from the 60s all the way through to the 90s. On Tuesday mornings, it was always a struggle to get up in time for my film class. On top of English Literature and Creative Writing, I had opted to learn more about *mise-en-scène* and French New Wave, amongst other things. I figured that if I never got round to writing that bestselling novel, I could be a scriptwriter instead. If that were the case, I would need to know all the jargon. Learn it I did, but I quickly had to accept that some of the finer points of cinema would be lost on me. I fell asleep in front of *Apocalypse Now*. And *Battleship Potemkin*. And *The Cabinet of Dr. Caligari*, despite the wacky, psychedelic settings. Our lecturer did his very best to criticise *Pirates of the Caribbean* at least once every lesson.

'It's like the McDonald's of the film world!' he would say.

Junk, basically. I liked junk. It stung a bit at first (nobody wants to hear their tastes are rubbish, especially from a university lecturer in the very first week) but I soon learned to live with it. A little bit of everything does you good.

Elsewhere, my Creative Writing classes were picking up; we were learning how to 'show' rather than 'tell'. I wrote an abysmal poem about big ideas of Love and Sorrow (emotions that read as capitalised are a definite no-no) for my first assignment and, from there on, I began to improve. Poetry was the real big discovery during my four years in Bangor. I had only ever written a handful of poems before the start of my course. Now, if I look in my folder, there are over sixty files. Several of my poems have been published and one of them got short-listed in a big international competition. A third of that elusive novel I'd been dreaming about is now written, with the rest simmering away in my head. I am glad I uprooted myself, at the age of nineteen, and moved to a different country. I think that my struggle to adapt and fit in, while simultaneously carrying around the memories of another culture and another life, was in great part responsible for shaping me into the writer I am today. I can safely say my work is a product of hybridity, reflective of the identity struggles that often take place within my own mind. Who am I? Where do I belong?

* * *

June 2010. For as long as I can remember, my mum had always talked about the possibility of me going to study at university in the United Kingdom. When I was little, I just shrugged and nodded, not really sure what it meant. I wanted to be an actress back then, or a singer, or a witch even. The only British school I wanted to go to was Hogwarts. Several years later, as we drove along the North Welsh coast and into Bangor, I looked up at the Old Arts building standing proudly on the hill and realised that this was as close to Hogwarts as I would ever get. I don't regret it. I have a BA in English Literature with Creative Writing and I'm in the process of finishing an MA in Creative Writing. I've had so many exciting adventures, gaining several great friends and an amazing husband-to-be along the way. By going to study abroad, I tore myself in half. Putting the pieces back together has proved to be the most intriguing and revealing puzzle of all.

Ten Rules to Stay British

Sin-yan Gloria Chan

Hong Kong/University of Birmingham

At the beginning of my life as an international student in Birmingham, I was encouraged to 'stay local'. 'If you stay local, your life here will be much easier,' was what I heard in the first session during my induction week. Because of this, I have always reminded myself to stay local, to try to live in a British way. One year ago, I would have told you that to stay British was to be decent, elegant, majestic and to have a 'British accent'. However, after living in Birmingham for almost one year, I would tell you ten rules to stay local in Britain, and they have nothing to do with decency, elegance or majesty, but surely with a British way of speaking.

Welcome to the life of an international student.

1

The first thing I would like to tell you is that British people have a special 'but' and they use it in a special way. Here is my experience with the British 'but'.

Nobody would disagree that living in Britain was not cheap and that was naturally the reason for me to keep searching for part-time jobs. The careers centre in the university was definitely a saviour to guide me. I made an appointment with an adviser from the centre. They held a 'CV clinic', assuming that our CVs were sick. However, when you were talking to them, you would usually hear:

'Your CV is already very good . . .'

Once you hear this, it's time to expect the British 'but'.

'. . . BUT we recommend that you should add your GCSE and A level scores to it.'

'Oh, I don't have any GCSE score. I am from Hong Kong.'

'Well, then you can add the UCAS Tariff Point to it. It is the standardised measurement of GCSE or A level scores in Britain,' my CV GP said.

'I have asked but UCAS currently doesn't allocate tariff points to my qualification,' I said, miserably.

'Oh, I am sorry to hear that . . .'

When you hear this, you should expect another British 'but'.

'. . . BUT you have to add your GCSE score or UCAS points to your CV in Britain.'

'I don't have any . . .'

'I understand that the UCAS point is a complicated issue. I currently don't know any other ways to convert your qualification into UCAS points. BUT I am sure it's worth trying to ask the UCAS unit,' my CV GP comforted me in an even more professional manner, as if the more professional she sounded the more easily the problem could be solved.

'Alright, I will try again then. What else should I do

to improve in my CV?'

'Well, I think your CV is good enough.'

'Thank you very much. Your advice is very useful. I much appreciate it,' I said.

'You are welcome. Wish you all the best in job application. And please don't forget to fill in the questionnaire and give us your feedback.' She smiled.

I moved on to the next room and left a glowing feedback on the questionnaire. 'Your service is already very good,' I added.

So, first rule to stay British: Know the British 'but'.

2

British people have a special 'but' and they like to put 'good' before it. So, if you want to stay British, it is important to learn this technique. I can show you an example here:

After spending half an hour in the careers centre discussing my does-not-exist GCSE points, I went to see my external examiner. All students in my programme were scheduled to meet our external examiner that day to give feedback about our course.

'It would be better if we could design our own topic for the term's essays,' a student suggested.

'Well, that's a GOOD idea,' our external examiner responded automatically.

'But?' I thought.

'BUT . . .' the external examiner continued.

'Bingo!' I thought, vindicated.

'. . . we will need to discuss more in-detail before we can do it.'

'I think the library resources are quite limited. I want to read more about linguistics,' another student said.

'It's GOOD to hear that you want to read more,' the examiner responded. 'BUT I think they have already tried their best to increase the book collection in the library. I hope you understand that it is also difficult to buy every book for every discipline.'

'Is it possible to replace exams by term essays?' Yet another student asked.

'That's a GOOD question,' our external examiner responded so wholeheartedly that for once I thought that it was really a good question. 'BUT I can't give you an answer at this moment, I have to discuss with the assessment committee,' she added.

You could probably guess what rule number two is: Use 'GOOD' and 'BUT' well.

3

Other than having a special 'but', British people are also very humorous. They are so humorous that you will feel bad if you do not laugh at their jokes.

At the end of the meeting with our external examiner, our Head of Programme said: 'Thank you all for coming. We hope that you have given us as much feedback as possible. After this meeting, you can go to the botanical gardens next door and enjoy the nice weather. I hope you find it worthwhile.'

Our Head of Programme was a typical British gentleman. He always looked trustworthy and calm, and spoke in a professional and decent manner. When he told jokes, he had the ability to ensure that people laughed, even though the jokes were not funny at all. But because of his British-gentleman charisma, we all laughed after he gave this ending note.

My third rule to stay British is: Learn to make people laugh by telling funny or unfunny jokes.

4

Once you move to Britain, you will start to love British tea. Therefore, after the meeting, we all went to the botanical gardens nearby to sit on the grass, sunbathe, and enjoy some tea. It had been raining for the past two weeks and we were all delighted to see the sun again.

'Hey, Adam, did you go back to Manchester last week?' I asked.

'Yes, I did. I went back home and saw my nan. She was ill,' Adam answered.

'Oh, I am sorry to hear that. How is she now?'

'Thanks for that. She's ge'ing be'er.'

'I'm sorry, she's what?'

'Ge'ing be'er.'

'. . . Alright.'

'Do you like the tea?' Adam asked.

'Oh, very much!'

Rule number four: Enjoy British tea.

5

I had a busy day today. My Hong Kong friend was holding a birthday party in Oxford and I had been invited. I mentioned that to my friends before I left the botanical gardens.

'Hey, Polly, I am going to Oxford and I have to leave you guys now,' I said.

'Oh, are you going to die?' Polly said.

'What?'

'Are you going to die?' Polly repeated.

'Hmmmmm, oh yes, I am going today so I am leaving now.'

'Al-rite, I will see you soon.'

'See you.'

Rule number five: Don't feel insulted when a Briton asks if you are going to die.

6 & 7

I got home around 2 p.m. I had to hurry since it would take me thirty minutes to get changed, twenty-five minutes to walk to the local train station and fifteen minutes by train to Birmingham New Street, the main train station where my intercity train departed.

I arrived at the local train station at 3 p.m. and was lucky enough to catch a train immediately.

'The next stop is Birmingham New Street; Birmingham New Street is the next stop.'

I looked at my watch and it was 3.10 p.m. I still had enough time to buy a Subway sandwich, I thought, and felt happy. I always like to have a Subway sandwich on the train.

Two minutes later . . .

'. . . I am sorry to announce that this train service will be interrupted due to . . .'

I could not hear the rest of the announcement. It did not matter since I knew the train was not moving and

I might not be able to catch my next train.

Three minutes had passed . . . The train was not moving.

Five minutes . . . and another five minutes. The train was still not moving. I became anxious. I would definitely miss my train to Oxford. I would need to buy a last-minute ticket which was much more expensive and I would be late for the birthday party. All these thoughts popped up all of a sudden and I kept looking at my watch.

The train moved again eventually. I looked at my watch; it was 3.28 p.m. when the train arrived at Birmingham New Street. I jumped off and rushed to check the train-departure board.

'Alright, Platform 2b.'

I immediately ran in full gear, jumped up thirty-five steps to the concourse, dodged three men and two women, hurdled two suitcases lying randomly on the floor, dashed down the stairs to Platform 2b. Then I heard:

'. . . We are sorry to announce that the 15.33 train to Oxford is delayed by approximately fifteen minutes due to technical problems.'

Thank God! I made it!

I believe whoever has lived in Britain knows that everything travelling on rail, road and air can be delayed due to many different technical reasons. However, the delays are very well-organised and consistent. They usually occur at the same time and with the same amount of time to ensure that you catch your next train.

Therefore I have my rule numbers six and seven:

Don't be anxious if you experience delays during your journey; delays always occur in Britain. Forget about missing your train; the well-organised train delays ensure the whole system work perfectly.

8

Britain is a technologically advanced country. Online service is so developed that you can do almost everything, including train-ticket reservations.

Every time I needed to travel, I reserved a ticket online in advance. I usually took one of the largest train companies in Britain, the Virgin train. The online-reservation system was very user-friendly and I could even choose between window or aisle seats online. Since I was an international student, curious about the scenery outside the train, I chose a window seat whenever I had to travel.

Virgin Trains was an enterprise that would never let its customers down. Every time I chose a window seat, I got it. Very often I got the 'window seat' between two windows. That meant I could literally see nothing, not even a window.

I had booked my ticket in advance and chosen a window seat as usual for my Oxford journey. After I had dashed down the stairs to Platform 2b and realised that my train was delayed for fifteen minutes, I delightedly and slowly took out my train ticket, strolled across the platform and got onto Coach A.

Coach A was a 'quiet zone'. I turned my mobile phone to silent mode and found my window seat. I sat down, looked right and faced a creamy white wall between two windows. I looked around the coach and saw three other passengers sitting in the 'in-between' window seats, and rows of empty chairs next to the windows. I then moved to a real window seat and enjoyed my journey to Oxford.

Rule number eight: Trust the online-booking system; it makes sure that window seats are available.

9

I arrived in Oxford at about 5 p.m. I was a bit early so I wandered around with my Hong Kong friend Debby. She took me to a nice milkshake shop where we could choose whatever ingredients would be blended. When we were in the queue she asked in Cantonese: 'How's Birmingham?'

'Well, not too good, not too bad. It's a good place for study though,' I replied, also in Cantonese.

'I am thinking about a day trip, so do you think Birmingham is a good choice?'

'I think it is fine if you want to do some shopping and visit some museums. There is not much to see otherwise.'

It got to my turn in the queue and I ordered a milkshake with After Eight and Oreo. When I showed my student ID to get a discount, the guy behind the counter said with a strong Brummie accent: 'Oh, are you fram Bh'am? I am fram Bh'am too! How do you *laike* it?' he asked excitedly.

'Oh, it's wonderful! I *laike* it a lot!' I replied immediately.

After I had paid for my milkshake, Debby asked:

'Is that what you have learnt in Britain?'

'Yes.'

Number 9: Be flexible.

10

It was time to party eventually. We had something to eat at around 7 p.m. while watching the England team playing in the World Cup, and then we went out. There were a lot of people in the club we visited, and many of them were wearing England football shirts.

'I don't understand why people are so crazy about football. I don't think it's exciting watching twenty-two guys running around a football pitch,' Debby said.

'I don't know, but I am a die-hard football fan. And as a person coming from an ex-British colony, I simply have the mindset to support the English team.'

'Then what about Britain? Do you like it out of your post-colonial mindset too?'

'Yes, I like Britain a lot. Perhaps it's my post-colonial mindset too. To be frank, I did experience some little troubles here. Then I reminded myself to adapt and I actually found those troubles funny. They just make me laugh when I think back.'

That night, I immersed myself in the British football crowd. I stayed until very late and I was dancing, laughing and singing.

And here comes the most important rule: Enjoy yourself!

The Conversion

Grete Brewer-Bakken

USA/Newcastle University

My plane lands at 2 p.m. I'm still screwed over from sleeping on the floor in New Jersey and I've got a bad headache, right between the eyes. The sun's out; I can't see the city of Newcastle upon Tyne from the airport, but I already have this feeling that it's nothing like London. I'm more tired than I've ever been, and here's Chris, trudging along behind me to the baggage claim, and I tell her all this information about London that's going to be useless here.

I need to get the lay of the land, right away.

My carry-on didn't make it through customs in New Jersey. Nothing new. Can't even cross a state boundary without being read article and subsection of our new human-rights laws. I wish stuff came cheaper these days. Replacing all my protective gear will probably require its very own Federal loan, and California's a little strapped for cash right now.

There are girls waiting for us in front of the airport, wearing white T-shirts with red writing. I generally love the British accent, but at the moment, all I hear is that I'm not in good ol' America anymore. The girls have a bus lined up, heavy duty with a grate across the front and bars on the windows. Makes me wonder if things here are worse than advertised. The driver shoves our bags underneath the bus. It's a nice day. The air smells clean. I'm headed to my flat at Claremont Place, but Chris needs to go by Accommodations and get herself squared away. Last I heard, they were still cleaning out the Grand Hotel from what happened there last year, cramming incoming students in anywhere else they can fit them until the place is liveable again.

I get a nice blue handle-bag denoting my international status and containing the 'Hi, how are yas' of Newcastle University. There's a Snickers bar (my favourite), a bag of salted potato chips, and a little sack of coffee, tea and sugar packets. At the very bottom, they've tossed in a sturdy-looking Taser with the university logo on it, and a red-and-white armband. I tie Chris's on her left arm and then let her do mine, just like the girls at the gate told us. The thing's going to fray away to nothing in a day or two, but it's just supposed to last till we get our university jackets.

I'm totally turned around by the time the bus heads up Richardson Road, past a nice-looking park and the field beside it. The field's surrounded by barbed wire on top of iron fencing and the grass beyond has gone all to hell, but the Keep Out signs are clean and new, and the fence looks strong. The bus window is dusty; I smudge it away and squint. There's nothing in the field, but I can see swans in the park.

Back in California, I asked my mom why they didn't just throw up concrete walls instead of simple fences.

She said that walls are all good, except for the part where you can't see what's on the other side. I guess it's better to know what's coming.

Chris stays on board the bus, but for me, it's a clunky trip up the walkway to the main office at Richardson Road, where I'm told the postgrads all have free bedding already in their flats. My new keys look so barren in my hands. First thing I'm doing when I get to my room is digging my handcuff key chain out of my luggage and gussying up this key ring a little. It has no character at all.

A guy and a girl in red and white offer to help with my suitcases. Turns out I live a freaking million blocks away. I wonder if I smell. I wonder if I look foreign. At least I look and smell alive. California has scanners and anal-retentive canaries at all the checkpoints, but I'm not sure what the everyday procedure will turn out to be here.

My helpers are friendly: they point out all the university-watch officers on the way to my flat, remind me to keep my armband visible, and gripe about constantly delivering people to fourth-floor apartments in buildings with no elevators. Luckily, I'm on the second floor – first floor, by local terminology. God, it's going to take me forever to get used to this. And the fire doors. I feel like I'm passing through cramped airlocks, one after another: from foyer to stairwell, from landing to hallway, from hallway to bedroom. They've all got slide bars on either side, and the guy shows me how to release the catch and clang the bar down into place. It's different from the ones back home. The catch on the door to my room is a little sticky, but it feels damn solid once it's shut, me and the guy on one side and the girl waiting on the other.

I release the guy and thank them both. They head outside to collect more newcomers, literally bouncing on their feet as they go. It seems ridiculous to me that anyone can be that energetic.

I do indeed have bedding. It's green, folded neatly on the mattress next to the standard red-and-white jacket. This is so not my room. It's *a* room, sure. Hard not to crumple under the lack of me on the walls.

I try on the jacket, praying that they've got the size right. I asked for extra large, and I really don't want to go through the same crap I went through back in Santa Cruz during the first of the USA outbreaks, when they gave me a petite uniform and I had to have an escort with me for a whole week while they tried to finagle the right sizes for all the mixed-up transfer students.

Don't even know if they offer escorts here. It might just be the armbands, laid out so the watch officers can recognise the university students.

The jacket fits, thankfully. A little tight when I zip it up, but I'm planning on dropping some weight over here, so it'll just be another incentive. My room's pretty small, but I've got two windows, which is more than enough to take the pressure off. There were 3-D virtual tours on the university website of rooms that had nothing but a skylight, and there is no way I'd commit to staying in one of those, the current state of the world be damned.

The bathroom is plain, the shower stall cramped. I bar the door and clean myself up. It feels insanely good to brush my teeth, to floss properly. All I want to do is sleep. No, all I want to do is get out of the room that isn't mine. Go find Chris, see if there's accommodation open for her or if she's going to have to bunk in a bed and breakfast. It's so stupid how useless I am without my cell phone. I went for ages without one in high school, not needing it at all, but now that I've lived on the opposite side of that fence, it's like I've lost one of my hands or an eye. An ear.

They've got lots of maps in my room, and a bulletin board with no thumb tacks. I don't even know where to begin in terms of shopping for those. Outside my windows, the drop to the ground isn't too high, and there's nothing to climb on either. All in all, it could be worse. I punch a needle from my travel sewing kit through the biggest city map and pop it up on the bulletin board. My lighthouse calendar will go right beside it, and underneath, photos of my family and friends. The map's key denotes safe zones and hazard zones in various colours. Newcastle city centre is blocked off in welcoming blue, but there's an ugly red blotch up near the top with the name Town Moor. I'll have to figure out where that is and take a look at the fencing around it. Get my bearings.

There's a ton of paperwork on the desk: fire-drill specifics, rules for living in the flat and taking care of the kitchen, cleaning schedules, and of course the standard set of logistics for evacuation. Mine's easy. I'm right above campus, apparently, so I'll just be heading down to the Percy Building, wherever that is. According to the packet, Percy's practically got a military bunker in its basement.

I'm more interested in getting down to the shops to

see what's available for my personal protection. The rules here are different in terms of the Draggers. I don't know if they're even called Draggers in Newcastle. I'm willing to bet things here are nothing like in Texas, with the gun-toting and vigilantism, but California is an agricultural state, and we've got poison and gas-weapon prohibitions because of that. Here in the UK, it could be something entirely different. I assume the Draggers are contained to the hazard zones or something. But whatever. All I want to do is be American today. And go find Chris.

In the morning, I read up and find out that, as a student, I'm insured to carry a low-level Taser, with the understanding that I will be sent back to the States immediately should I use it for anything other than the legally stated purpose. They also let us have some sort of nerve spray, and both the Taser and the spray have meters to track when and how they're used. The meters are linked back to campus security; one spray, one shock, and they'll know something's going down and where. I remember when my biggest worry was being harassed by random guys on the street at night. Almost makes me wish for that again, just to prove that we're succeeding in cleaning up this mess.

I'm inside O2 getting my new SIM card. Chris is outside because I've been a bitch. It happens when I'm tired. Stressed. Makes me feel like such a loser because, as she tells me when I finally get my shit together and come outside, we can't turn against each other. We're all we've got here. She's crying, and then

I'm crying, and I don't care that we're in the middle of Northumberland draped all over each other right in front of the O2 store and every person in the city. At that moment, I just want to go home.

There's a lot we have to buy: wall-socket adaptors, food, toilet paper, soap, and a million other things that we won't realise we need until we get back to our flats, I'm sure. Shopping's a pain in the ass. There's no sense of personal space here. Seriously, people just walk straight into you and bounce off like ping-pong balls, and then sometimes they blame you for it. Manoeuvring through Marks and Spencer is a nightmare. It's not even that crowded, but I can't find what I need and none of the brands are ones I recognise. I want to pick up a simple box of Honey Nut Cheerios, but even that's different here.

Chris needs coffee, and to get her cell phone unlocked. My left arm hurts like a bitch from the inoculation this morning. It's not a real inoculation; you can't exactly inoculate someone against a chemical threat. The shot is some protein that enhances the body's resistance instead, and the needle was the biggest I'd ever seen. But my frustration really comes to a head later when I try to call my mom and discover that the guy at the store gave me a texting SIM card instead of what I asked for. Mom gets cut off a minute into our conversation and now Chris can't use my phone either. I'm this close to the breakdown I promised myself I wouldn't have. Chris sets up her campus internet access so at least we can email the fact that we're alive, that the city is safe and that we have places to sleep that aren't outside.

Why the hell did I come here anyway? And why did I have to drag Chris along with me?

They have a strict zero-strikes policy on racial harassment here according to the police officer we meet the next day. It took a little while to get through security at the King's Road Centre, but that's mostly because of the sheer number of students. I'll admit it: they've got a pretty efficient system here with the dogs and the scanners, and not once did I hear any barking. It's a relief I didn't know I needed to feel.

The meeting room is packed. Everyone's required to attend at least one of these sessions this week, and I wonder how many students will be reprimanded for missing their scheduled meeting. I don't feel sorry for them. If I can make it while I'm jetlagged beyond belief and feeling like the most pathetic being in existence, then they can make the effort, too.

The officer passes out a thin booklet on campus security, a card with important numbers on it that we can stick in our wallets, and a personal alarm keychain with an LED light on the end of it. We get it all in another useful handle-bag, and then she gives us a fat booklet on city-wide catastrophic emergency and evacuation procedure. An email will be going out later with a link to a quiz, she says, and we're all required to complete the procedural counselling online or our student cards will be revoked.

The first page of the booklet is this weird cartoon drawing of a sexless person suffering from a number of ailments. I recognise most of them: headache, jaundiced eyes, muscle spasms, fever, hallucinations. But there are a couple I haven't seen before. In California, blotchy skin isn't a telling symptom, and complete loss of vocal capacity is definitely new. There are emergency phone numbers on the bottom and a list of other minor symptoms to watch out for. The affliction symptoms seem to come on a few days faster here. Either that or they're just being extremely careful. I've heard the lawsuits in the UK for bad diagnoses have been appalling, even worse than in America, and that's saying something.

There are a lot of Chinese students here, more than any other group, or so I understand. I watch them nodding along while the officer talks about policy, and the little differences between the human-rights laws of the UK and the laws in other countries. I can't imagine what it must be like to listen to life-saving information in a language that isn't your primary one, especially a language with such varied accents. The idea alone scares me to death. What would happen if I missed something? What if I misunderstand and everything goes to hell because of it? What if I get killed, or get other people killed? These students sitting around me are so much braver than I am. I practically have a mental breakdown when I can't make out the Geordie accent, and here they are, potentially not understanding entire sentences while sitting calmly and quietly. I'm not an idiot, I know that what's going on inside isn't being broadcasted to the rest of us. It's still an achievement I can't even fathom.

Afterward, I head back to the mobile-phone store and exchange my SIM card. The guy puts a refund on my online account. I'm so tired and it's been hot, which means I'm not sleeping well. I want a nap. But I can't; I have to go get my picture taken for my student-access card, and then Chris and I are scoping out the pub outside her building for dinner. The Grand Hotel is once again open for business. The place smells like brand-new paint, completely sterilised. Maybe they sprayed the walls with bleach. The Grand Hotel doesn't have a lift either, and Chris is on the very top floor. Of course. All I can say is that we're going to have gorgeous calves in about a month. I've already decided to call a cab when I head back to my flat. It's just a few blocks, but it's past the overgrown field, I've got groceries, and I finally figured out that I live a lot closer to the Town Moor than I thought.

Dinner's good. Lasagne like I haven't had in a long while. It's different enough from my mom's lasagne that I can avoid any homesickness. The pub quiz of the week is on, and Chris and I are doing pretty well over in our corner, considering we don't know jack about the next big thing in this country. I'm getting that sick feeling I get when I don't sleep enough. Who the hell programmed my stomach to hurt when I'm low on sleep? It doesn't make any sense at all; there's no way to connect one to the other except through the accidental trial and error I managed when I was ten. Tomorrow, Chris and I sign up for medical-care providers, so I'll have to make sure I put this anomaly on my facts sheet. Otherwise they'll probably deport me as one of the afflicted.

The positioning of Chris's flat is both good and bad. On the top floor, nothing's going to come crawling through her windows, but it's also a long way to the front door. She shares a single-sized room with another girl, but all we've seen of the other girl so far is a bag of clothing on one of the beds and a suitcase wrapped up in duct tape and twine. The Grand Hotel is close to the city centre, but my building is right up on the big red Town Moor blotch on the map, so I'm in worse shape in that department. The Moor is across the road, hidden behind a line of trees. I haven't gone over to take a look yet, take pictures, whatever. Figure out how safe I really am. But I suspect there will be double fencing, possibly electrical. They wouldn't put students so close to a hazard zone without taking extra precautions, that I'm sure about. Too many legal ramifications if something goes wrong. My flat's got people from at least five different countries in it, and I know that the UK doesn't want to mess with governments who end up missing their international students.

The cab driver is quiet, and my fare is really low compared to London. At these rates, I could call a cab whenever I need one. I'm tempted to ask him about the affliction and the Draggers here, what they're like. What they're called. But I've never been good at making small talk. I always see myself as an imposition.

I wonder if the Draggers in England can climb. Probably not, because the fences around that one field didn't look too high-tech. It depends on what all went into the chloride fertiliser mix over here. Everyone's got different Draggers. They're pretty standard in America: slow, stupid. Persistent. I hear that Japan's got runners, though, and the ones in Scandinavia can still solve simple problems, like window latches and door knobs. Down in Mexico, the Draggers aren't really threatening at all. They're just there, slumped against walls, rotting away on the corners of intersections and waiting for the HazMat teams to come clean them up. I could have gone there to grad school, but I was afraid of the language barrier. I don't speak any Spanish despite having lived in California my whole life. Mexico would have been closer to home than this, though.

It takes me a half hour to figure out my internet connection when I get home again. I've already blasted my way through two power converters because I'm an idiot and bought the wrong kind. I feel extra stupid because my computer has its own converter. I Skype Mom a message and wait until she comes on. But it's too late: I've already started crying when her face pops up. That's my home there over her shoulder, with sunlight and a messy dining-room table, and Loki, all ginger-coloured and sweet, wagging his tail in the background. It's too hard to keep up a stoic, mature front in the face of Mom's patient questions.

I tell her I've got all my shots, that my flat is pretty claustrophobic, and that Chris has a place to live. I tell her about the Taser, and the bag full of condoms they handed out to everyone at orientation. It's damn funny, actually: they're all the colours of the rainbow. I tell her about the thumb tacks Chris found for me in the Student Union, and the family photos I've put up, how I've got three years of my sister's school headshots to look at. One of them's a magnet; I've got a little fridge in my room, but no one told me if I'm allowed to use it. I read something about having to rent the individual mini-cools and I assure Mom that I'm headed down to reception in the morning to ask.

She asks about the affliction over here, the Draggers. I tell her not to worry. The buildings here are state of the art; the university looks after its students, and they've got gorgeous German Shepherds at every checkpoint. I'm pretty sure that eventually I'll see a Dragger, that the alarms will go off and things will happen in the streets outside, but I've read up on the procedures and taken the online counselling. If all goes to plan, Newcastle's got the affliction well in hand.

Final-Year Crisis

Adji Hafiz Sjadzali

Indonesia/University of Exeter

'Look at you! You're white!'

Jealousy is common in my family and it did not surprise me that these words came out during a family gathering. In Indonesia, as in many eastern Asian countries, women desire bright, shiny skin that is of course elusive given the intensity of the sun all year round. 'If only my skin was whiter I would get the man of my choosing,' their minds go, or 'My husband would come home early if only . . .' and so on. Not surprisingly, whiteners are popular and readily available at a *warung* – that is the traditional shack store – near you.

Despite being a bloke, I have made a lot of women jealous with my glorious skin. Their eyes fix on my forearms, especially the under-sides, as the veins that carry my blood visibly resemble a river, giving my forearms a look most people could only achieve by doing labour under the Bolsheviks. The fact that all of us in that stuffy living room were connected by blood or law had only made the jealousy worse. We have all shared the same family history, both being there for each other in times of need and tearing each other apart on a game of Charades, as extended families tend to do.

'What's your secret?' one aunt asked, following with a sinister smile-cum-laugh.

'Seriously, how did you do it?' another one asked, but this one with a sort of half-joking desperation that reminded me of Bogart as he parted from Bergman in that last scene in *Casablanca*. Her frail body was the colour of the sands in Kuta at sundown, poised there as she sat on the ground on the outer part of her right thigh, sweet and calm.

I have found myself in situations not so different to this many a time, these having mostly occurred during the family gatherings we had almost every week. These meetings would alternate between my father's side of the family and my mom's, but once in a while I would enjoy the company of both sides. There wasn't any reason in particular that would bring us together. Sometimes it's a family meeting, other times it would be for food. Once, for my cousin's wedding, we all gathered almost every week and would rotate the responsibility of being the host among the families. We discussed who was going to do what at the wedding – who was responsible for the catering and all that. The question that often came out during the wedding meeting was, 'Who shall we invite?' A furious debate would usually ensue.

'The so-and-so definitely should come!' one would say.

'Oh, please, no way will that whore come to this family's wedding!' another one, usually my mom, would reply.

Finesse and subtlety runs in the family but there are

times when the heart speaks louder than appropriate diction.

I took it to myself to try to explain the truth to these people, that I had not done anything special except taking regular showers each day as my method of achieving this admirable complexion. I suggested that they should do the same but my remarks were met with pinches by my aunties.

'What is this jealousy? It's not my fault that you've all missed my European lineage,' I joked. In reality my features could not be further from European. My jaw dominates my face and my nose is small and tucked in thanks to evolution that perhaps allowed my ancestors to inflict less damage to themselves when they ritually ran into things face first. In profile, I resemble more a Neanderthal than a *Homo sapiens*, my chin being the first part of me to cross the line if ever I was involved in a race.

The simple fact was that my enviable skin could be attributed to nothing more than lack of exposure to the sun. At this explanation one of my aunties yelled, 'Absurd!' with a conviction none of us had seen in her before. She insisted that I must have applied a scrub or a cream to my skin, at least something. I rejected her hypothesis and explained that the only thing I've ever applied to myself outside of the shower was the rain that blocks the sun itself. Pushing things a little bit further, I told her that all that English rain washed away the dirt that would have made my skin darker. She looked at me with a heavily strained eyebrow and dismissed me by laying a word on the table: 'Absurd!'

* * *

About a week after that meeting, I got on a plane and headed back to the UK. I was going back to do my final year at the university. The year preceding I had been in Brussels for an Erasmus exchange programme. Having been away for a year, I started to realise the small things I had missed about Exeter. I remembered the two years I had spent in this little city before I went to Brussels. Walking in the city centre it was so easy to bump into someone I knew, a friend of a friend I'd met somewhere. Sometimes I felt like a local star being greeted by so many people on the streets, and such level of familiarity was not often displayed in a big city like Brussels.

But that was then. Exeter has changed a lot in the space of three years. The first time I stepped foot in it I thought to myself: 'What have I got myself into?' Having been used to living in Jakarta and then Oxford for a couple of years, it made me wonder whether Exeter was a town or a village. That first year in Exeter, entertainment was scarce and there was not much to look forward to in the city. One long stretch of a high street with familiar retail stores could hardly get an urban citizen like me excited. Slowly, though, things picked up. The retail area expanded and suddenly the high street was not the only commercial destination in the city.

So, for my final year I had to again get into that small-town rhythm and limited options but I never thought it would be a problem. I've always been good with people and I make friends easily. Since I went for the Erasmus exchange programme, friends of mine who did not opt to take the scheme carried on with their degrees and by the time I was back for my last year a lot of them had graduated. Suddenly, my rapport-building abilities were needed more than ever and as the year progressed it became evident that as I drowned in a pool of essays and assignments, I needed friends the most. Of those people I'd known from the previous two years, only a handful were still around. My new classmates, most of whom were a year below me the year before, were hopeless. They seemed so distant, unable to interact with people outside of their social groups. My batch was better. At least that was how it felt to me.

I was determined not to let my shortage of friends bother me and put as much effort as possible into getting into the swing again. One of my most comforting routines before I went away to Brussels was to munch on the Cornish pasties that they make really well in this city, particularly the ones from Queen Street. Their availability and affordability led me to have them pretty much every day for lunch. I've always liked them and I think they are one of the best things to ever come out of this island. A pasty is a thing of beauty. My father told me once that during the coal-mining boom in the South-West, miners' wives would make these pasties so that their husbands didn't have to surface to eat lunch and by holding the thick crusts they could munch on the rest of that thing without getting their dirty hands on the part they ate. Genius! Innovation at its best. Not only that, they taste pretty good, too. As with anything, balance is crucial and I found the moist filling inside combined with the crispy pasty to be a taste of heaven. I was very glad that I could get back to doing this again but for some reason it was just not the same. Something was still missing.

It got to a point where I became really bored with going to the same place every day. I was hoping at some point as I walked into that pasty shop that everyone would go 'Adji!' like they do in *Cheers*. There would be one postman sitting down eating his steak-and-kidney pasty complaining about his wife at home and his boss in the office. I'd pick up my steak-and-blue cheese pasty, bid *adieu* to everyone and walk out the store followed by a song about a pasty shop where everybody knew your name. But no. It was always dead quiet when I went to this shop and every transaction was like the first time I went there.

By winter, I was knee deep in essays and other forms of write-up, the library was my second home and I became good friends only with academic journals and my MacBook. In the late nights the only source of light in my room was my computer screen. I was not surprised when the birds and the squirrels played outside to indicate the start of spring that my vision was becoming worse. I've had glasses for many years and I progress to more powerful ones almost every year. However, I have learned that increasing the power in your glasses to match your deficiency only makes things worse. It's like when you fish and use a bait to lure the fish towards you. Matching the power of your glasses with your eyes lures you towards higher and higher power. Before you know it, you end up with glasses thicker than your aquarium. That's how I got my minus three on both eyes anyway. With that power, it is enough for you not to recognise faces at distances beyond twenty metres and reading bill-boards is a nightmare. All the while, the lack of light penetrating the thick English clouds and rain did little to help me recognise what lay ahead. Another thing that they did was block the UV for most of the time. I noticed that my skin turned whiter still but clear and matted as well.

Time flew by and before I knew it the last of my exams was finished and summer officially began. Of the very few friends I had during the year, most of them left for the summer vacation. Four years of higher education with a rigid schedule full of lectures and tutorials suddenly was no more. I ended up spending the days reading and cooking and eating and watching movies from the university's library. When the weather was good, I would take a book outside and go to town for coffee. The Exeter Cathedral Green was a nice place to lie down and do some reading. Despite the ocean of unoccupied students on the Green, it could maintain a calm quality, perfect to relax. On one of the really good days I and some friends who were sticking around until graduation got on a train to go to St Ives.

St Ives is a small beach town south-west of Exeter. When we got there, we were on top of a hill and looking down we could see its famous stretch of sand tucked away below us. The sun was generous that day and the light reflecting the bright sand and the deep blue of the waters was truly like a painting. Tourists were in abundance and from afar they looked like freckles on a face. We went down the hill and eventually got to the waterfront. The sand was so dry and soft it barely stuck to my skin as I ran on the beach. We found a peaceful spot next to a young family struggling to build a sandcastle.

'The sand is too dry,' I told them. 'You should move closer to the water.' The mother acknowledged my opinion and took her kids fifteen metres closer to the sea.

The light that day was harsh but it did bring out many colours rarely seen in this part of the world. Pristine blue sky, even deeper blue of the ocean, the custard-like cream of the sand and the greens of the hills. They were in themselves a sort of visual entertainment and yet provided a serene ambiance for meditation, that is, if the process of natural tanning does not bother you. I could feel the tingles on my skin as the sun slowly baked my soft, white skin, turning it darker. We brought books and board games to pass the time but when we snapped out of our relaxed mood we had forgotten all about them. The sun was taking an angle and a whole new spectrum of colours took over. The sky looked much closer and the horizon seemingly walked away from us. Clouds were beginning to warm up, radiating a soft glow of orange.

For a while my mind flashed back to those times when my family and I were back in Indonesia, enjoying the sunset on the beach. In that flashback I felt something. I felt at home but then it occurred to me that perhaps I was feeling like home never existed in the first place. Or maybe, even, at that moment, I wasn't quite sure where home was. I don't know what it was but something was stirring in me. In truth, I have felt as comfortable in the Northern hemisphere as I have in the Southern, and sweating under the tropical sun is as unpleasant as shivering in the European winter.

'Hey! I'm gonna grab some ice cream. You want some?' a friend of mine asked, snapping me back to reality. I nodded. He went away to check our options and came back.

'They have chocolate and vanilla. Which one do you want?'

I looked at him and was not at all impressed by the options. I didn't know what to make of it. The chill started to come in and the warm sand underneath me was now cool. Light was fading fast and the magic of that beach drifted away with each wave hitting the sand. It's just ice cream, I thought to myself, but I couldn't stop feeling upset. I wanted more options. These two options in that beach in St Ives seemed boring, separated only by a huge void between the polar opposites. What happened to the spectrum of options to choose from?

I shook my head. 'Nah, it's getting dark. Let's just go home.'

Danielle

Ahmed Elsayed Fetit

Egypt/University of Birmingham

The bar was loud and welcoming, the chatter and the laughter filling the room with love and ease. Xavier Stephan stood by a table against the far wall, deep in conversation with his peers about the night they had planned ahead of them. Occasionally, he raised his glass to his lips to take another gulp of the cool beer. Sunlight streamed in through the windows, falling in broken rays across the varnished wooden floors, and Xavier turned his head to look outside, squinting against the brightness.

That was when he saw her, the prettiest creature he had ever witnessed; God's most perfect creation, a goddess of the most divine beauty amongst the living. His heart raced in his chest and the words he was about to speak caught in his throat to escape his lips as nothing more than a croak. He was stunned, rooted to the spot like a sentinel, and he smiled. He saw her drag on her cigarette, blowing out a thin stream of smoke from perfectly full lips as the wind picked up speed and blew her hair to one side of her face, and Xavier had never before seen such beauty confined within one body. The sunlight caught her flawless face, handcrafted by the heavens, and the butterflies in his stomach evolved into enormous eagles, beating their wings furiously. With every step he took bringing him closer to her, Xavier felt his knees buckle as he fell under her spell. He longed to have her as a part of him . . . to breathe her, to ingest her and to float away with her, their bodies entwined as one. What he would have given to touch her milky brown skin and run his fingers through the auburn hair falling in cascades over her slender shoulders.

'Excuse me,' he started. 'Could I borrow your lighter?' Her piercing blue eyes burnt into him and he was held, transfixed by her gaze.

'Sure,' she said, smiling, and rummaged about in her handbag, pulling out a silver Zippo and flicking it open for him. He jumped at the opportunity to feel his skin against hers and, cupping his hand around the dancing flame, he lit up his cigarette.

'Thank you.'

She snapped her lighter closed and took another long deep drag of smoke before letting it out slowly, closing her eyes to savour the flavour.

'I like your accent. Where are you from?' she asked, keeping her eyes on his at all times.

'I'm from Mexico,' Xavier said. 'I'm still trying to find a way of fixing my accent so that you people can understand me the first time.' He flashed a sheepish smile and leaned against the wall in a subtle attempt to make his image match hers in perfection.

'What do you mean "you people"?' she demanded, returning a full-toothed smile, a full array of thirty-two perfect tombstones, pearl-white gems. Not expecting an answer, she continued, 'What's your name then, Mexican?'

'Xavier,' he managed to choke out while exhaling. 'Xavier Stephan.' He extended his arm to shake her hand, again just wanting to feel her skin. 'Nice to meet you, um . . .'

'Danielle,' she answered through an exhaled cloud of smoke. 'Are you always so formal, Xavier?' She took one last puff from her cigarette and threw it aside, taking no notice of where it landed but focusing all her attention on him.

'Only to strangers.'

'Well, stranger, I have to go now. But maybe I'll be seeing you around.' She started walking away from the bar but then stopped and turned. She raised a hand to shield her eyes from the sun. 'Hopefully I'll see you at the club tonight!' she called out, and tapped her wrist where she wore the same wristband ticket as he did.

Danielle and Xavier began spending more and more time together as the winter days passed. He was a long way from home, but having Danielle with him seemed to ease his homesickness. Things just weren't the same in England for him, and Xavier was finding it difficult to adapt to such major changes. Even though he loved his home and country dearly, Xavier and his family knew that staying in the eastern Mexican state of Veracruz for his university education would not bring out his full potential, and that it was time for change. He had always been a good student throughout his high-school days, and for his last four years the Mexican government had granted him a scholarship for his academic brilliance in Mathematics and Music. This came as good news to his humble family because his parents, Jesus and Manuella de Vallo, who both worked in the export business of tobacco and sugar-cane, were already struggling to save up enough money to send Xavier abroad to study, regardless of the country or subject he chose.

August had come and Xavier was accepted to study Mathematics at London's prestigious Imperial College. Leaving his parents and friends at the airport was hard but exciting for him, for he had never left Mexico before. He had seen many wonderful things about England on television and the thought of actually going to live there and start a new life on his own kept him excited on the entire flight to Heathrow Airport.

After his first few days of settling into his accommodation and buying all that he needed, Xavier began to feel homesick. The clouds above that brought the thundering rain beating against his window kept him up for nights wishing he had stayed in Veracruz where the heat and humidity would force him and his friends to the beach. He was not accustomed to the absence of sunshine and it depressed him to the point where he would only walk from his room to his lecture hall and back, until he met Danielle.

England had never seemed so full of life and smiles before Danielle became his own personal tour guide, taking him around London whenever they were both free from studies. He felt elated walking around the streets with Danielle by his side, sometimes even holding her hand. He enjoyed noticing the women looking at them with jealousy and the men with lust, and they only grew closer and closer together. Everything seemed to finally fall into place. He had fallen so blindly in love with Danielle that he lost contact with most of his friends back in Mexico. Danielle became the sole purpose of his stay in England. Never in his life did Xavier think he would feel so strongly for a girl he barely knew.

After the first night Xavier and Danielle spent together, she told him about her little secret as she lay naked in his arms. The world around them was dark, and the only noises they could hear were each other's heavy breathing and she could feel his chest rise and fall rhythmically under her head as she rested against him.

'I don't even know why I told you, it's not a big deal.'

The tone of her voice was one he had never heard before and they had been seeing each other almost every day for the past month. It felt like she was ashamed of her habit, but she did not understand that whatever the circumstances, Xavier would not go anywhere without her; he wanted her for herself, not for who she pretended to be in the presence of other people, for Xavier still believed it was only him and her in the world.

'I want to try it,' Xavier said, a definitive authority in his voice which meant there was to be no further discussion on the matter.

Danielle looked up at him in silence but she could not pick up any hint of doubt or hesitation. The boy wanted what he wanted and who was she to stop him? Feeling selfish, it made Danielle feel good that she was not the only student at Imperial College to have chosen such a socially disapproved path. She reached up to kiss his lips and he returned the kiss, the last innocent, pure kiss he was to ever give another soul.

Watching her set up their heroin fixes, Xavier began to doubt himself. He did not know what he was getting himself into but the needle gleamed in the moonlight and he was fascinated, drawn to the idea of leaving this world with Danielle, even if only for a little while. From what he had heard about the drug, the soul leaves the body and a complete state of exhilaration takes over the mind. His hands began to tremble ever so slightly as he watched on, but his mind was still certain of his decision. *Solo esta una vez*, he told himself. Just this one time won't do any harm.

The days turned into weeks, the weeks into months and over the course of time, Xavier fell faster and faster and the honest life he had once lived was tainted by his new habit. He became a regular user, regardless of whether he was with Danielle or not, and he perfected the injecting process, never puncturing a vein, never forming a heroin blister. He began neglecting his duties to his family, losing contact with them for days on end and not caring whether they called at all or if his mother was crying because she was so worried. He began to drop the friends he had made from his course and from his dorms, extra weight he was not keen on carrying as he soared higher and higher on heroin.

May was creeping closer and closer and the end-of-year exams were only a few weeks away. Xavier woke up alone in his bed, severe cramps in his stomach, and he doubled over to vomit in a bedside bucket containing fast-food wrappers, dirty needles; the putrid smell of various bodily fluids filled the room. Over the months, he had slowly rendered himself useless. He would go days on end locked up in his room, oblivious to the conditions in which he was living. The bed sheets were stained with blood droplets and vomit, the carpeted floors littered with cigarette butts, papers, wrappers, bottles and cans. The only spot kept clean was a little corner underneath his desk where he would shoot-up and start working on his mathematics. It was the only aspect of his life not suffering the consequences of his decisions.

Xavier watched anxiously as Danielle opened the little plastic wrapper, his whole body trembling in anticipation. She was an artist to watch and as hard as it was for him to admit to himself, he hoped one day he would be able to set up his fix as gracefully as she did. The heroin she had bought was labelled Black Tar, and for the price of £20 a dealer would sell one portion of the drug the size of two Tic Tac candies placed side by side. She looked up at him.

'I want to fly,' she whispered solemnly, placing her hand on his knee. It felt cold and comforting against his skin and he closed his eyes, treasuring the feeling. 'I want to fly away, Xavier. I don't want to be able to see anything beneath my feet and I want you to come with me.' On that note, she emptied a second wrap of heroin into the spoon she was holding, a faint smell of vinegar drifting into his nostrils. The little white mountain of heroin beckoned him, its imaginary voice in his head summoning him to the skies.

'I don't think that's a good idea, you told me you already took some this morning,' Xavier pointed out, hoping to talk some sense into Danielle. He could tell from her eyes that there was no going back on her desires. He glanced at the heroin, at Danielle, and back to the heroin. 'Dani, please think of what you're saying. If something happens to you, I wouldn't know what to do with myself. Don't do it.'

'Nothing's going to happen. Do you know why?' She didn't wait for a reply. 'You're going to be right here to catch me if I fall, I trust you. And I know I'm being selfish for wanting to do this, but just let me.' She rested the spoon carefully on the wooden floor of her apartment and sat next to him on the bed. 'It would mean a lot to me if you understood this and sat here with me. I love you so much, and I would only let myself go with you here.'

As appealing as her offer sounded, it was the weekend before his final exam and he had no intention of failing. He remained watching her as she squirted water from a syringe onto the heroin and heated up the spoon with a lighter. Xavier could sense her rush, for usually she would roll a piece of cotton up into a little ball, dip it into the heroin solution and suck the drug with a needle before injecting herself. This time all she did was tighten an elastic band around her bicep and look up at him, smiling.

'I wish you were coming with me,' she whispered.

Xavier watched on, the muscles in his arms tightening.

The elastic band unravelled. The needle fell from her hand. The next few moments occurred too fast for Xavier's liking. The world seemed to shake. He wanted to move, he wanted to help her, but his body seemed frozen in fear. Danielle gazed lifelessly at him through miotic pupils and she fell onto her back, convulsing violently. Xavier's heart pounded in his chest.

'Danielle!' he finally called out, and leaned off the bed to hold her. Her lips were parted, her face pale, and it seemed as if she was looking out into the distance, beyond her ceiling and beyond the clouds on which she was floating as he cradled her head in his hands. A tear fell from his eye, a slowly tumbling tear carrying with it all the feeling of regret, guilt, self-loathing and disappointment that Xavier was harbouring inside himself. He could feel the warm droplet cling onto his upper lip before falling once more, landing softly on Danielle's face. He managed to get Danielle standing, throwing one of her arms around his neck, and he tried to walk her about while he could feel her muscle spasms against his body as he held her close. He could not help but blame himself for her condition but in the back of his mind he knew that taking the blame would not save her.

As he reached the front door to Danielle's modern, central London apartment, he pulled out his mobile telephone to call the emergency department. With Danielle barely conscious and her body limp, Xavier managed to walk down the stairs and outside to the pavement where he could hear the ambulance in the background. He felt as though his heart would beat its way out of his chest, and his temples were throbbing. Danielle had vomited on the way down and yellow bile was all over her chin and clothes. As the siren's wails grew louder, he rested her on the pavement and looked into her eyes.

'You're going to make it through this, Dani. They're coming now.'

The ambulance came to a screeching halt in front of them and three paramedics ran to their aid. Asked what had happened, Xavier told them she had overdosed on Black Tar heroin – he knew that honesty could save her life, regardless of what happened to him. Out of paranoia, he had expected the police to show up as well, ready to arrest him, but to his surprise they were nowhere in sight. He felt a sting of disappointment, for a part of him wished to be locked up in a place where the pleasure of heroin was only a fantasy for the foolish.

With his head bowed low in silent prayer, Xavier begged the Lord to look down upon them and save them from their sinful ways. He rested his elbows on the edge of her hospital bed and kept his eyes closed, her soft rhythmic breathing assuring him there was still hope for her life to be spared. All around him, the smell of detergent disguised the sickening metallic aroma of blood which would render even the strongest of stomachs nauseous, and even the smell of disinfectant seemed to have permeated into the wooden window frames. He tried to clear his mind of the smells and images he had witnessed over the past three months and enter a state of complete tranquillity where it would be only him and God, but all his efforts were in vain.

After crossing his chest, Xavier opened his eyes and looked up at Danielle. He remained kneeling and took her hand in his. He no longer felt the warmth and life that radiated from within her, and it saddened him. He could not help but feel pity for Danielle as she lay in bed, skin pale as snow. She looked frail and weak in her hospital gown, and Xavier feared that her hand would break if he squeezed slightly. He lifted his gaze to the bend of her arm; there were several red puncture marks around her median cubital vein and images of the past few months played through his mind like an endless slideshow of pain.

'It's all in my head, all in my head,' he repeated to himself as he sat nervously in the waiting room of the hospital. He felt ashamed of himself. He no longer cared about his appearance, and the once athletically built and handsome Xavier had been reduced over time to a long-haired, unshaven, scrawny street boy. He smelled foul and his clothes were dirty, stained with blood droplets and littered with burn holes. He struggled to keep his sleeves down to cover up the needle marks, but no one needed to see evidence of intravenous abuse to tell that he was using.

The nurses had asked him to leave Danielle's room after he said his prayers, and now all he waited for was the 'man who plays God', and Xavier raised his head to see him walking towards him. His long white coat and the bright fluorescent lights of the hospital made the doctor look like a celestial being, an angel, and Xavier jumped to his feet.

'Mr Stephan?' the doctor asked, slowly taking off his reading glasses and folding them onto his shirt. He was an old man – mid-fifties perhaps – with shiny silver hair and a slight limp to his walk. His breath smelled like cheap filter coffee.

'Yes, doctor. What's happening? How is Danielle?' Xavier demanded, his voice shaking in unison with the rest of his body. In his mind he was still praying, asking the Lord for forgiveness and for mercy.

'I'm pretty sure she's been better, lad. She was barely breathing on the way here and the paramedics administered a subcutaneous shot of Naloxone, or Narcan, as you may know it. Luckily, you called when you did. A few more minutes without it and she would have died. Anyway, she'll be fine in no time. We have to keep her overnight for observation but she'll be able to leave by morning.'

'Thank you, doctor!' Xavier exclaimed and before he knew it, he was hugging the doctor, who could not help but give out a chuckle despite the repulsive smell. Once he pulled back, the smile faded from the doctor's face and Xavier had never seen a more serious expression before. He knew what conversation would follow and decided to make it short to save himself the embarrassment. 'We're going to get into rehab, Dr Spruce. Like everyone else, I thought we'd be able to control it but I realise it's not possible. I know everything I tell you is confidential,' he continued, lowering his voice, 'and I'd appreciate if it stayed that way because I can't afford to lose more than I already have. My exams are on Monday and I was just wondering if you could prescribe me something I could take for the next week, just so I can stay focused enough to do well.'

'Are you asking me for a replacement drug for your heroin, Mr Stephan?' the doctor enquired, arching an eyebrow.

Xavier felt like he was shrinking under the doctor's glare and hoped the ground would open up and swallow him whole. Never before had he been so ashamed of himself or felt so miniscule, but he could not help it. It's all in my head, he thought again. *Dios mio*. Save me.

'No, sir,' he said. 'I'm just asking for a painkiller for my head, it's killing me.' He managed to smile and the doctor nodded, understanding fully.

'Right, this way, Mr Stephan.'

Just as he had asked for, Dr Spruce prescribed him Relafen for his migraines. Xavier was so mentally determined to ignore his cravings for heroin that his withdrawal symptoms were almost insignificant. He treated them like he would any other sickness, with hot tea and his migraine medication, and his mind was focused on his studies, for he did not need more than a day to pass his exams.

Danielle was released from hospital and after a long discussion, Xavier convinced her to join a programme because she did not have the self-control he did. They decided it was better for both of them if they did not see each other for a while and since summer vacation was coming close, Xavier thought going back to family and friends in Mexico would help them both. Gone were the days when they would lie in each other's arms, when they would shoot-up together and fall asleep side by side. England had taken its toll on him, but he was determined to fight back for what was his. He owed it to his family and friends to make up for the pain and grief he had caused them, and most of all, he owed it to himself. He wanted to prove that he was worth more than the £20 he would normally have used to buy heroin.

He passed all his exams with honours, gave up drugs and was ready for a new chapter in his life with a new haircut, shaven face and a clean soul.

'Thank you, Lord, for granting me another chance. Thank you for the strength to fight through the harsh times and for giving me a family that loves and cares for me. Amen.'

He took one last look at the person staring back at him from the mirror and smiled; clean for almost five weeks. He felt presentable; his family would be proud to see their son. He flattened his shirt against his chest, fixed his collar and wheeled his luggage out of the international Airport of Veracruz and into the Mexican sunlight.

'I'm glad to be back, Mama,' he whispered into her ear as he hugged her close to his heart.

Crossing the Lines

Muhammad Idzwan Husaini

Malaysia/Newcastle University

Two friends were walking up a narrow path in the middle of a green field. It was such a lovely day; the sun was out. In Newcastle such a day was a rarity even in the summer. There were many cows dotted here and there among the grass, grazing or just sitting on the ground looking at passers-by. Among the usual brown, black, white, black-and-white cows, there were around three that were grey in colour. That was a shocking thing to see. Grey cows were rare, abnormal even. The grey cows were grazing far from the herd and the two friends joked that the three cows were being discriminated against because of their weird coat. These friends should have been able to detect a display of discrimination; they made up the small proportion of international students at Newcastle University.

'Abang, I'm so jealous! Are you *really* going to see your *boys* in London?' Claire said in a voice that suggested disbelief. There was a note of surprised admiration in her tone for this guy she called 'Abang'. It literally meant 'brother' in Malay, and girls normally used the word as a term of endearment for their boyfriends. In Claire's case, the use was purely platonic; Adzim was gay.

'Yeah,' Adzim responded. 'Imagine, lots and lots of hot boys.' Adzim ended his sentence with a laugh.

'Are you gonna get *jiggy-jiggy* with them all?' Claire shot another question.

'Maybe,' Adzim replied, flashing a somewhat naughty and gleeful smile.

'Abang, you're so cheap –'

'What's *cheap*? I'm an adult,' Adzim said. 'I want to go to London and I'm trying to save some money so they offer me to sleep at their places and if we're having *fun* while I'm there,' Adzim gestured the inverted-coma sign with his fingers at the word 'fun', 'that's because we have consented to it. It's not like I'm offering them sex in exchange for a place to stay. I'm not cheap like some other gays in Malaysia.'

'There are gays in Malaysia?'

'Yeah,' Adzim said. 'I'm one.'

'Yeah, *lah*, but you only come out here. How do the gay people meet each other? I thought it was not allowed? I thought gay people would be stoned or something.'

'Of course it's not allowed, *lah*, but you can't really stop people doing what they want.'

'So, have you ever been with any gay guys back in KL? How did you find them?'

'Yeah. KL is like the capital of gay. You just go online on any gay websites. There are lots. That's why tourists like to go to KL. There are many students who would have sex just to get money and their customers are normally old guys.'

'No way! Really?'

'Yeah, that's how they can afford all the nice clothes and shoes. And they change their handphones like every three months. Seriously, their student allowance can't pay for all of that. They can get around RM 300 for just a one-night stand and that is just around £50. Those old guys probably don't mind paying that much as long as they get to fuck some tight smooth ass. I'd never do that.'

'Have any old guys made you an offer?'

'Yeah. They were super disgusting. Fat and old and bald. And they had lots of hair on their chests. Eurrghh! If I'm going to have sex with anyone, it would be because I'm attracted to them. I know it's shallow and all but at least I'm not getting paid for it.'

'But you don't even know them,' said Claire. 'How do you know that they're not some crazy murderers? Later I'll be reading the news on the front page: Malaysian student found chopped to pieces in the heart of London.'

'Fuck you! I know how to look after myself, *lah*. That's why I chat with them first.'

'But did you see their faces? Did you see them on cam?'

'Yeah –'

'Oh my God, are they cute? Are they hot?' Claire cut in. She was clearly excited. 'Abang, did you guys have *jiggy-jiggy* on cam? Did you guys wank? Can I see?' Her curiosity was at its peak.

'See what? Us wanking?'

'No, *lah*. Their faces, *lah*.'

'I'm not gonna show you. They're *my* boys.'

'Abang, I wanna see . . .'

The remainder of the conversation was Claire begging Adzim to let her see the people he had been chatting with as the two friends continued walking up the path with the sun still shining gloriously high in the sky.

There was a knock on the door.

'Come in,' Adzim said while his eyes were still on the screen of his laptop. He and Claire were on the bed in his bedroom. They were both looking at something on his laptop.

'*Oh my God,*' Kathryn pretended to squeal in a girly voice. 'Are you guys making babies again? Can I join?'

'Go away, *lah*, we're busy –'

'Oh my God, Kathryn,' started Claire, 'have you seen Abang's boys? They are all so cute and hot!'

'Boys? How many do you have?' Kathryn asked Adzim.

'He has like five of them,' Claire answered, 'and they all have nice, hot bodies. I'm heartbroken.'

'*Really?* Have you seen them? Dude, why didn't you ever show me?' Kathryn rounded on Adzim. She tried to take a peek at the laptop but Adzim managed to shut the screen.

'Why should I show you? Stop being jealous, *lah*.'

'He was on cam with two of them and they were both, like, really really buff!' Claire said. 'God is so unfair. Abang is not even good looking. I don't know how he could get those guys.'

'Oh please, you're just jealous,' said Adzim. He put the laptop aside and walked out of the room to sit on the couch in the living area. Claire and Kathryn followed Adzim like two paparazzi.

The living room was messy with open boxes and luggage strewn all over the place. It was summer break and the inhabitants of 9 Belle Grove West were busy packing to go home to enjoy it.

'So when are you going to London?' Kathryn asked as she resumed her place in front of one of the boxes, wrapping plates and bowls and putting them into the box.

'Early July,' Adzim responded while wrapping the couch runner around his skinny body. Although it was pretty warm outside, the inside of the house was still chilly for Adzim. For someone who had spent the first twenty years of his life in the tropical country of Malaysia, Newcastle's cold weather was something he was still not used to, even after two years. The heating in the house was not switched on. They were just students and the UK was the island of rip-offs, especially for international ones.

'How long are you going to be there?'

'Probably like two to three weeks. I'm gonna explore London. I've seen the touristy part of London so this time I'm gonna check out the city itself, taking the Underground and stopping at some random stations with weird names. And then I'm gonna go shopping. I can't wait for the summer sale. And yeah, I'll probably go watch a play or two.'

'I want to watch *Phantom* again,' Kathryn said. 'And I want to watch *Love Never Dies*. Who are you staying with?'

'I'm staying at a friend's place. An actual friend,'

Adzim added defensively in response to Kathryn's 'yeah-right' stare. 'I do have friends in London. And even if I do sleep at some other guys' houses, it's well within my rights. You two are just jealous because I have all the hot guys.'

'It's so unfair,' Claire said. 'Why is it all the cute and hot guys are gay?'

'That is so true,' Kathryn agreed. 'If a guy is hot and cute, he's probably gay. If a guy is nice and sweet, he's probably gay too.'

'Yeah, and they are always the ones who are most successful,' Claire added. 'And rich. All the straight ones are jerks. And chavs!'

'But seriously, people were born gay, right?' Kathryn asked.

'How should I know?' Adzim responded.

'What about you, Abang?' asked Claire. 'When did you realise that you like guys?'

'I was watching porn and I realised I got turned on by looking at the guy more than the girl,' said Adzim while sniggering.

'Did you ever like girls?'

'Yeah, when I was like twelve.'

'But that doesn't really count,' said Kathryn. 'Do you ever look at a pretty girl and start thinking: "Damn, she's hot!"'

'Nah. When I see a pretty girl I will go like "Oooh, she's pretty" but I never feel like asking her out. I think in my case it was more like a choice. I do like girls but I don't think it's fair for them that I have feelings for guys. So I just choose to be completely gay, *lah*.'

'But then that proves the point that being gay is

innate,' Kathryn said, 'because you somehow don't feel that you're being unfair enough to the guys for liking girls to cause you to choose being straight completely.'

'I guess. Whatever. I know I like cocks.'

'Yeah,' Kathryn said gleefully. 'We know you like it big, and hard.'

A rush of footsteps was heard from the landing of the staircase before Ali came down from upstairs dragging with him a heavy suitcase.

'Can you girls please stop talking about cocks?'

'Oh, I'm sorry if the topic is a sensitive one for you,' said Kathryn.

'Yeah, I forgot you don't have one,' Claire added to a smattering of laughter.

'Oh please, you two lesbians,' said Ali taking a seat on one of the steps of the stairs.

'Ali, who's coming to pick you up?' asked Claire.

'My parents are on their way. What were you guys chatting about?'

'Abang and his gay-ness. Abang, how was your childhood?' Claire asked. 'Did you get bullied a lot?'

'No. I was the one doing the bullying.'

'Seriously, what is wrong with everyone in this house?' said Kathryn. 'Ali was such a bully as well.'

'What? It's not my fault that boy was fat,' Ali said in defence of pranks he had played on a boy when he was in school. 'And it's not like you never bitch about your friends.'

'Yeah, don't complain, *lah*,' Adzim said. 'That's how we all got here. It's either because we're bullies or bitches. It's all about survival of the fittest. The fact that we bully or bitch about people suggests a degree of competitiveness that gives us the edge for success. That's why we are here. Cool Asians studying in a world-class university.'

'But that is just horrible,' said Kathryn.

'Nah. It's part and parcel of growing up,' said Claire. 'If you can't fight back or come up with a good come-back, then you'll lose, *lah*. And yeah, if you can't beat them you join them.'

'Yeah, I was lucky at school,' Adzim said. 'It helped to be clever, *lah*, because the teacher favoured me and made me a prefect. So in a way, I was in a position of power and I got to be part of the in-crowd. I was not *exactly* abusing my power.'

After more discussions on how each four of them survived the competitive nature of their high-school years, someone knocked on the door. Ali got up and went to open the door. The other three became quiet like young people normally do when they know their friend's parents are about to invade their comfort zone.

Mr Tanvir walked into the living area smiling genially to everyone in the room. Adzim got up from the couch to shake hands with Mr Tanvir. As Claire got up to shake hands with the man, he retracted his hands.

'Oh, I'm sorry. We cannot shake hands. In Islam, we're not allowed to shake hands with people from different gender.'

As Claire uttered a barely audible, 'Owh,' Adzim managed to exchange a glance with Kathryn that screamed, 'Awkward!'

Of Chinese and Filipino parentage, Claire had been

exposed to a variety of cultures while growing up in the Philippines, Hong Kong and Singapore. While she had encountered many Muslim friends in Singapore, the idea of a practising Muslim family living in the UK was something she did not think possible.

'So,' Mr Tanvir said to break the uncomfortable silence, 'when will you all be flying home?'

Adzim was last to reply. 'I'm not going home. I'll be staying here. My parents are going to Mecca in July so there's no one at home. Plus, we'll be starting clinical year end of August so I thought it's better just to stay here to sort things out.'

After some polite exchanges of goodbye, the Tanvirs left 9 Belle Grove West.

'Abang,' Claire started, 'I didn't know guys and girls can't touch hands in Islam. I seriously didn't.'

'Yeah, you can't.'

'But I've touched all my Muslim guy friends in Singapore. I've touched you before.'

'Well, I choose to be gay,' Adzim retorted. 'Supposedly you can't but people make their own choices.'

Adzim was in the bed leaning against Lee's broad chest with Lee's huge arms hugging Adzim's slim body. Naked, both had the kind of freshness one would normally have after showering. They had in fact just showered after a raunchy threesome in the kitchen. Lee's hair was still damp.

'So, how do you like threesomes?' said Lee. 'Did Ant and I live up to your fantasy?'

'Yeah,' answered Adzim. He caressed Lee's arm as

he said, 'It was the best.' He reached up to kiss Lee's lips most passionately before resting his head back on Lee's chest. There was a look of satiety, fleeting and momentary, on his face. The silence was broken a second later when Ant came out of the bathroom, drying his naked muscular torso, saying:

'Aww, you guys are making me *really* jealous getting all lovey-dovey in *my* bed while I was showering.'

'We're waiting for you,' Adzim said apologetically. 'Get in the bed quick. What took you so long?'

'Well, sweetheart,' Ant said as he crawled onto the bed on all-fours. 'It took a while to rub off all the honey and chocolate. Damn, the thing we do to fulfil your fantasy! I think I deserve a good kiss.'

Adzim released himself from Lee's hug to make out with Ant. The passion he had had when kissing Lee was not present.

'I'm sure it was worth all the trouble.'

'Definitely,' Ant said before planting another kiss on Adzim's forehead. 'So which part of Malaysia are you from? Is it the same as Lee?'

'Nah, I'm from KL.'

'It's like five to six hours driving from Penang,' Lee added.

'So, you've had fun tonight?' Ant asked Adzim. 'I bet you now regret not trying threesomes sooner.'

'He said it was the best sex he's ever had,' said Lee.

'Yeah. It was good,' said Adzim, 'but I'm not regret-ting anything. I'm glad that my first threesome was with you two.'

'You've had lots of sex in Malaysia?' Ant asked.

'Not really. Not everyone is open about it. Plus, I

only accepted my sexuality like a year before I came here so there wasn't much time to explore.'

'So you've had lots of sex in the UK then?' Ant pressed further. 'I bet there are many hot jocks in your university who'd love to have you ride their cocks.'

'Not really. I'm always busy with assignments and revision. Medicine fucks my life! But at least life has been easier, *lah*. I can at least come out to my friends here.'

'Yeah, I know what you mean,' Lee said. 'It's harder in Malaysia. You have to keep it secret because you can never tell who'd be willing to accept the fact that you're gay. There's always a chance that the person you trust might blab about it to some other people you don't want to know. It's riskier if you and your siblings have the same circle of friends.'

'So no one in your family knows?' Ant asked.

'Nope,' Adzim answered, 'except maybe my brother. I think he once saw me looking at the gay website I used to look for other gays. He didn't talk to me at all for like a week. But he just kept it quiet. We're OK now.'

'Lucky you,' Lee said. 'My brother told my mother straight away. And here I am. I haven't gone back to the country for a few years now.'

'I'm so sorry,' Adzim said. He then took the chance to kiss Lee's forehead. He thought it was best not to ask too many personal questions on the first night of his stay.

Lee changed the subject. 'So you'll start your clinical year soon?'

'Yeah, end of August. It's going to be one hell of a

long year. But it's OK, *lah*. We'll be in hospitals all year round doing some *actual* medicine. I'm tired of going to lectures nine to five every single day. It'd be a good change. And who knows, there might be some hot gay doctors in the hospitals.'

'Well, you are always welcome here, in this bed, whenever you're in London,' Ant said.

'That's good to know. It's going to be a very stressful year so I might come down here to relax.'

'Do come,' Lee said. 'We know how to help you relax.'

'The tuition fee for the year is expensive though.' Adzim changed the topic. 'The fee for international students is like eight times more than for home students.' I know some guys from my college who did not get the minimum qualifications but still got accepted after appeal. I'm pretty sure the university just wanted more international students for the money to come in.'

'That might actually be true,' Ant responded. 'This country is really going down the drain. The money is being spent all over the place.'

'I know,' Adzim agreed quickly. 'I really don't know why the chavs are even allowed to live. They spend their whole day hanging out at the park. Don't they go to school? Don't they have assignments to do? They're such racist bastards. And they live on benefits and their parents don't even go to work. My neighbour spends her whole day sitting at the front door smoking in the same ugly bathrobe every single day.'

Ant laughed heartily. 'That might be a stretch but it's true.'

'Yeah, but who cares?' Lee said. 'Why are we wasting our time discussing chavs? Three horny guys in a big bed and we're talking about chavs?'

'Oooh,' Ant cooed, 'I think Lee has something else in mind.'

'Really?' Adzim said. 'What do you have in mind, *hottie?*'

'Just you,' Lee said before he rolled on top of Adzim to kiss him sensually.

'I'll switch the light off,' Ant said as he reached for the switch on the wall.

'Abang, how was it?' asked Claire. It was September and the new term started with the usual recollections of sunbathing at exotic beaches and backpacking through tropical countries and interning for a magazine and many other thrilling escapades.

'How was what?' Adzim responded. 'The sex? They were good!'

'*They*? How many did you have?'

'I was in London for more than two weeks. And I stayed at different places.'

'Abang, what do you get from all that?' Claire asked. 'Just sex? Or have you chosen one of those guys to be your boyfriend?'

'Just sex.'

'But I thought you wanted more.'

'Yeah, but you can't start a relationship just by chatting online for a few times. They're in London. Too far for anything serious. So we all agree that we're just friends. I still chat with them'

'But you can have sex just by chatting online for a few times?' Claire argued cynically.

'The thing is it's hard to find love. Many gays have given up looking for relationships. What's the point of having a relationship when we can't go out together holding hands? Or kiss each other in public without being judged and condemned as freaks? We have to do it in secret and, in the end, it feels like having a secret affair just the way many straight people do. We have to do it in secret and in the end, it feels like having a secret affair. It might have been easier in this country but people still look at us like we're some weirdoes. Sex is easy. We just stay in bed to show how much we love each other.'

'But, it's not really love. Is it?'

'Maybe not. At least we *like* each other well enough that we're willing to share the same bed. That's why I don't mind doing it because at least I can be honest about my own feelings and desires. If I were to walk into a coffee shop with another guy we would have to deal with everyone staring at us as if we are disgusting or smell really bad. And that's not the worst that can happen. In public, I'll have to behave in certain ways and act in certain manners and talk about certain topics.'

'So you would rather just be in bed with gay guys you don't know,' Claire asked, 'than to be in public because people might recognise you?'

'You see, I don't like those guys because I can have sex with them. I don't have to pretend I'm somebody else with those guys. They make me feel comfortable in my own skin. I don't have to pretend I'm somebody else with those guys. That is really funny because they're strangers but at least they don't judge. What's ironic is that I have to pretend among my friends and family when they should love me and accept me unconditionally.'

Day Thirty-Six

Ahnaf Abdul

Malaysia/University of Oxford

Even the sun sparkling on the frost couldn't make the word CUNT look good. Someone had scrawled it in the snow on the stone table, with a few FUCKS for good measure. Alison hadn't noticed. She'd gone straight to the wall, where you could look out over the white blanket of Christchurch meadow, and was snapping pictures.

In its own way the crudeness was impressive. Whoever had done it must have woken at dawn on a Saturday morning, confronted the first snow of the year, and decided that the appropriate reaction was toilet graffiti. Probably the rowers, I thought. Though to be fair, I couldn't see them around. Or anyone else. Too early for them, and for me too, if Alison hadn't practically kicked my door in while squealing: 'Snow! Snow! Snow!'

We'd rushed out without even dressing properly, so that for the last half hour I'd been wandering around in a bathrobe and slippers. I could feel my feet getting wet. The camera's memory was getting full, too.

'Do you want to go in?' I asked.

'In a bit,' she said. She turned to say something then saw the table with its assortment of profanities and rolled her eyes. 'Mature.'

'Wasn't *me*,' I said. I scuffed the words and drew a giant smiley face instead. After a moment I added fangs. Alison wiped down the bench, which also had its share of FUCKS. You'd expect more from students here – I know I had when I'd started a few weeks ago – but it just wasn't the case. I suspected the admissions process confused smartness with quickness. Students at Oxford weren't any smarter than ones I knew elsewhere, but we were a hell of a lot quicker. At doing dumb things.

Alison was looking at the meadows again and saying something about painting. I half-listened as she chattered happily about light and shade and whether she should just do a pencil sketch or go all out with watercolours. I wished I was artistic. If I was, I'd paint the trees decked in icy finery. I wondered how they felt. To wake up one morning, leafless and naked, encrusted with snow. The cold would sting. It'd be like waking up to a hundred piercings. Trees weren't her subject, though. Alison always drew girls: nymphy, waify, moody ones. 'You could do the Narnia girl,' I mused.

'What?' she said, derailed.

'Isn't she at Magdalen?'

'Who?'

'The Narnia girl. The older one, I mean. You could bring her here,' I said, pointing to the stone table. It was supposed to have inspired C S Lewis's stone table, where Aslan was sacrificed in *The Lion, the Witch and the Wardrobe.* 'And you could get someone to dress up as a lion.'

'She'd probably charge,' said Alison. Then she shivered. 'Are you cold?'

'*Yes*,' I said. My slippers were soaked, although the bathrobe had held up surprisingly well. She handed me her camera and said she'd check her *pidge* before meeting back at the house. Both the pigeon-hole room and our house were in college, but at opposite ends. It was a bit odd to see her walk away – she'd cropped her hair and dyed it green, making her the only green thing in the garden. I should buy her some red beads. Or ribbons. I didn't know if she'd appreciate having her head look like a holly bush, but it would be very seasonal.

I walked back to the house, keeping to the edge of the garden to avoid scarring the smoothness of the snow. It really was beautiful. Later – after the snow had been scooped, packed, thrown; after it had been slipped on, skidded on, slid on; after it had birthed angels and a snowman who lasted for weeks; after it had made little blue flakes appear everywhere on weather forecasters' maps; after it had received its own live blog on the *Guardian*; after it had ground an unprepared country to a freezing halt; after it had buggered the pipes so that I didn't shower for X number of days; after it had cancelled lectures and closed libraries and been secretly praised; after it had been trod on and kicked off and openly cursed; after it had become slushy and manky with muddy dribbles – I would learn to be sick of it.

But later was days away. I was still only an hour into

my first snowfall, and only been in England for five weeks. So I knew nothing.

When I got back, there were two texts waiting. I checked the first. My mother. I realised, to my surprise, it'd been two weeks since we'd spoken. Was I avoiding her? I didn't know. It just felt better not to think of home. Whenever my thoughts strayed in that direction they seemed to meet some huge, impassable thing, not hard but definitely firm, like the wall of a bouncy castle. A castle all to myself.

The other text was from Percy asking about brunch, which I replied to instantly and instantly felt guilty. Opening up the text from my mother, I sent one back asking if she could Skype in the morning. Singapore was eight hours ahead, so that would mean staying up tonight. Still, the next day was Sunday and I could lie in till brunch. And Percy.

There was clattering in the kitchen and I went to check if Alison was back. As I got closer I could smell eggs frying in sesame oil. Li An was at the stove, in a black tank-top and faded grey track bottoms, prodding at the beginnings of an omelette. I got the soy milk out – Alison was vegan – and Li An glanced up. She quirked her eyebrows in acknowledgement and looked down again.

I only called her Li An in the privacy of my head. It was Leanne otherwise. The name-card attached to her door said Choo Li An, but after she'd moved in, it had been struck through with a thick black marker and 'Leanne' written above it. Li An was a mystery but Leanne wasn't. Leanne had studied in England for years. Leanne spoke in a Cheltenham Ladies' College accent. Leanne moved in a languid stroll. Leanne always had a cool, heavy-lidded sort of expression, the kind affected by people who've seen too many things to bother seeing more.

Her room was directly above mine. It probably wasn't a coincidence, since we were the only two Singaporeans in college – though I wondered what the Accommodation Manager had thought would happen. Perhaps she expected us to breed.

I shuddered.

'Something wrong?' she said.

It must have been a very visible shudder. Oops. 'Just cold,' I said. 'Been out in the snow. It's very pretty, isn't it?'

She lifted a shoulder in a languid quasi-shrug. Leanne would have seen snow many times, of course.

I filled the kettle. 'Tea?'

'No. Thanks.' She tipped the omelette out onto a plate and started frying sausages. She was hungry, obviously.

I sniffed and looked longingly at the omelette. Then I frowned. 'Is that my pan?'

She paused. 'Oh.' The pause stretched a few more seconds, punctuated only by the awkward sizzling of the sausages. 'Sorry.'

'Never mind,' I said, minding very much. Luckily my phone beeped then, pre-empting a resurgence in the Cold War. Mother again, saying she'd look forward to Skypeing at half-nine her time, half-one mine.

I poured the water into two mugs, dumped the

teabags in, and let them brew. The sun was stronger now, and through the window I could see it reflected dazzlingly on the snow. If I squinted I could also make out the path of size-nine prints my slippers had left. Alison was coming up too, holding a few envelopes.

'Oh hi,' she said, noticing Leanne as she came in. She put her mail on the counter and picked up her mug. There were quite a few letters. I felt a twinge of irrational envy. I'd have to tell friends back home to send letters too.

'I bumped into James McTaggart just now,' she said, with a 'Look'. No conversation about Boys ever began without a Look, and James McTaggart, a third-year chemist, was definitely a Boy. I didn't think he was that fit but Alison liked the tall, lanky type.

'And?'

'Apparently they've sent out info about the varsity trip,' she said. 'Asked me if I was going.'

'I'm going for that,' Leanne put in unexpectedly. Her going on the trip was to be expected; Leanne had probably skied right out of the womb.

'Do you know how much it is?' Alison asked. 'I've never been skiing.'

I sipped my tea while they talked. I wasn't yet sure of my plans for the winter hols. The trouble with existing in two worlds was that you could never live fully in either. By the time I confirmed whether or not I was going back to Singapore the deadlines for everything else here would have passed.

Not that I was particularly enamoured with the idea of the Oxford–Cambridge varsity ski trip. I was quite attached to my limbs, and the company didn't appeal. The locals had to be very tolerant to put up with a horde of Oxbridge undergrads each year. At least, the type of undergrads who probably went skiing: ruddy-cheeked, barrel-chested, back-slapping carousers heehawing to each other across the slopes, no doubt. Maybe that was how you turned into a Real Oxbridge Boy. Maybe ski resorts worked like that Pleasure Island in *Pinocchio*, only in reverse, so that jackasses turned into men. Then I felt my own Jiminy Cricket put a stop to that uncharitable line of thought.

They were talking about James McTaggart now, though I could see Leanne had finished cooking and was loading the remaining food onto a plate to bring back to her room. Without washing the pan, I noted grimly.

She was about to leave when, almost as an after-thought, she said, 'I saw Percival the other day.'

'Percy,' I corrected automatically. I knew he was bizarrely proud of having such an old-fashioned and romantic name, but it didn't do to encourage him.

'Yeah, Percy,' she said. 'I think he was in the queue outside Babylove.'

She was expecting me to ask when. I could feel it. She expected me to ask when so she could then say Tuesday, knowing full well that I knew that Tuesday at Babylove was gay night and, yes, Percy and I both being male and newly dating, it would be unusual for him to have patronised such an establishment without my knowledge.

'Oh,' I said.

She was looking at me. The sun shone on her face

from the window behind me, making her expression unreadable.

'I didn't see you, though,' she said finally. 'Guess you were inside.'

'No.' *Bitch*.

'Oh. Well, I'll wash your pan later,' she said, and left. I looked at Alison. She was making porridge and hadn't seemed to notice anything out of the ordinary. She was that rare thing, really – a perky Brit. The British could be jovial, genial, or even convivial, but as far as I could tell perkiness usually bounced around in stars and stripes on the other side of the Atlantic.

Her hair made me smile, and I felt the bile subside. If she'd cottoned on to the exchange just now she'd probably have been mystified by the rancour. Even I didn't quite understand it. Of course Leanne was a Chinese Singaporean and I was a Malay Singaporean, but that was hardly worth mentioning compared to our common roots. Or were those roots the problem? Maybe when Leanne looked at me she saw what she had once been. I looked at her and saw what I could be. Either way, it seemed, we didn't like the sight.

The good thing about cocktails is that you often can't tell you're drinking alcohol. The bad thing is that you often can't tell how much alcohol you're drinking. I'd had three. Maybe more. In any case I felt a bit giddy. Pathetic, but in my defence it was on an empty stomach. I'd vowed not to cook until the pan had been cleaned, but by the time that happened it was already time for drinks.

That sounds misleading. I don't mean to imply that I was some sort of habitual drinker. Notwithstanding religion it was simply cheaper to stay away from the stuff, and easier to get sloshed if sloshing happened rarely. That Saturday evening fit into the 'rarely' category, since some law firm had suddenly decided to give our college law society £1000 on the tab at Raoul's, apparently out of the goodness of its corporate (limited liability partnership) heart.

I gathered this wasn't unusual, at least before the recession. Nothing breeds affection like inebriation. I could feel myself looking kindly down on the world of corporate law, buoyed up on the froth of a Very Berry Jerry. Studying Law was like being a prostitute – the wined and dined, un-trafficked escort kind, anyway. A debutante, then.

The room was stifling, though. Raoul's was cosy at the emptiest of times, and cramped when filled. The room they'd hired was in the basement – all low ceilings, high stools and loud speakers, with only one narrow exit leading upstairs. Everything was red too, because the only light down there was a sort of scarlet wash. All it needed was someone to start stripping and it would have been a scene made for the tabloids.

I fought my way to the bar. 'Can I have a General Lee, please,' I said.

The barman had his hands busy mixing half a dozen drinks at amazing speed, but spared a grimace in my direction to show he couldn't quite hear.

'GE-NE-RAL LEE, PLEASE,' I said, louder and slower. Bloody music.

General Lee was made with cucumber and raspberry

vodka. Refreshing. I tried to figure out who to talk to. The third years and half the second years were clustered around people from the law firm. The other half were mingling with the first years, who were really the only people I could name. There was Terry, on the right side of the exit, talking loudly about something. I couldn't actually hear him, but his mouth was opening wide so it must have been loud. It shut again and he made some sort of pumping movement with his fist, then opened hugely in what must have been a very loud laugh. I was sure I could see spit. He should keep his hand in front of his mouth. All that spit. I sipped some more of my General Lee and was about to tell him about his spit when someone squeezed my arm.

'Are you having a good time?' Rebecca smiled. Her eyes were bright.

I opened my mouth, remembered the barman, and carefully said, 'YE-ES.' I was going to add something else but she smiled and squeezed my arm again and slipped into another circle.

I didn't follow her. I didn't feel like trying any more circles that night. I was tired of circles or any other two-dimensional shapes. I was tired of the bloody music that forced me to repeat myself in what Alison called my bloody 'sing-song' accent which nobody bloody well took seriously because English people speak in a sort of flat chesty way that goes down at the end of sentences instead of lilting up. I was tired of being jostled by people I barely knew in a little red room.

There was a bigger room upstairs with people I didn't know at all, of course, but even though I'd had enough liquid courage to strike a conversation, it would end up either with me repeating myself or being told my English was very good. I was tired of *that*, too.

I downed the rest of my General Lee. Take that, General! I thought, and marched to the exit.

Terry saw me going and called out, 'You leaving, mate?'

I stopped and faced him. He was four feet away. I nodded and then, inexplicably, bellowed, 'HEEHAW!'

There may have been laughter after that, although I can't remember. I can't remember getting back to college either, although I remember checking my empty pidge and then staring suspiciously at the toilet lid. Obviously I was lucid enough to remember it was a BoP night. 'BoP' stood for 'Breach of the Peace' but was basically the equivalent of a school disco every few weeks. After the last BoP I'd been traumatised by a toilet bowlful of unpleasantness, so the closed lid confronting me then was a bit of a gamble. I don't remember lifting it, but it must have happened eventually since I didn't piss on the bed.

And I did get to bed. I know I did since I remember turning to lie on my side and face away from the wall. During freshers' week the welfare committee had warned us about people getting so smashed they choked to death on their own puke. It was exactly the sort of silly thing people here would do. Back home I would be chatting with friends over *pratha* and *teh tarik* out in the night air. But the weather here was silly, even if the snow was pretty, and a good time here consisted of drinking so much you forgot you ever had a good time. And possibly died.

But I wouldn't die. I was different. Wasn't I? I shifted

and lay on my back. I was pure. I hadn't eaten that day, too. If I puked there'd be none of that shitty biological gunk, it'd be pure, pure and clear. I pursed my lips and then widened them into a small 'O', a small spout. Above me, the ceiling was swaying and I imagined wetting it with all the pureness that was in me, that was rising through me out of my lips in a fountain of clearest vodka. Then I realised the ceiling wasn't swaying but the floor was. The floor was swaying because it was the sea, swaying indivisibly throughout the whole world. And I was floating on it, an island between continents, adrift.

I always kept a bowl of water beside my bed. I had no idea whether it was scientifically plausible, but I had the vague belief that it would evaporate and keep the air moist, and hopefully stop my skin from drying out. When I woke, that bowl was the first thing I reached for, and drank.

My lenses were still in. I blinked several times, hard. The clock came into view – quarter-past one. Almost time to call home. I could hear soft footsteps and a clink, then a patter of typing and silence. That would be John in the next room, also doing Law. He'd told me before that he often worked late, taking a sip of port in between typing and reading. I often thought he might end up as an overworked, substance-abusive barrister. I nodded approvingly. The old ways were best.

I took off my tie but kept the jacket on. It was cold, but I opened the windows since the room felt stuffy.

Not enough. Everything felt small. I put on my shoes, grabbed my laptop and went out.

By the light of the half-moon I could still see the fanged smiley I'd drawn that morning was still there on the stone table. Someone had added horns. Unfortunately most of it got scuffed as I climbed on top of the table and sat in the middle. I left my laptop on the bench, signed into Skype – you had to register for it, but there was actually a Wi-Fi signal in this part of the grounds, which the college was awfully proud of.

Behind me the garden bore the signs of a day criss-crossed with boots and snowballs, while before me the meadow lay as it had that morning, white and untroubled, spreading out to the distant shadows of trees in frost. I took my left sock off and wiggled my toes on the table, packing the snow onto each tip until my foot looked like it had sprouted five sugared walnuts. Maybe I should take off all my clothes. I could stand and take them off, and in five hours or so the sun would rise, ponderously, and its dumb, slow rays would reach me and refract, refract beautifully, through the ice on my body. And then the college could buy some freezing machine to put at my feet so I could stand forever over the garden, over some little spot of my own in the world – like Jeremy Bentham's stuffed body in UCL, except much more glamorous.

Of course there was always the risk everyone would think my naked ice-encrusted body was just part of some kink. That'd be humiliating. It would be like those boys you found hanging in their rooms, literally dying for a wank. People would find me, find my laptop, then put two and two together and get pi. Someone needs to invent a program that wipes all the porn from your computer as soon as you die.

I brushed the snow off my toes, put my sock on again and apologised to the air. It replied. In fact, it tooted. Then I realised it was the Skype ringtone and picked up my laptop.

'Hi *sayang*,' my mother said, then frowned. 'It's very dark.'

I paused. 'Blackout,' I said, tentatively. Then I repeated it, more confidently. 'I'm on battery.' I angled the screen and the eye of the webcam towards my face and hoped she couldn't see much else.

There was another pause as I tried to work out what to talk about. Coursework, maybe. Not Percy. Not flecks of spit made vivid by vodka on an empty stomach. Not vodka, in any way. Definitely not Percy. There wasn't much to go on, then – had there ever been much? What did I ever talk to her about? School, maybe. The siblings. Distant relatives. Local politics. The odd movie. Things I hadn't realised I was leaving behind. Things that kept moving, leaving me behind.

Luckily, before the silence dragged, she started talking about taking my sister to her first violin class later in the day. I listened. I talked. Mostly I shivered. It was strange, really, to think of one part of me here and another part of me thousands of miles away. And my voice, which I could hear bits of, crackling out of the speaker on the other side – where did that belong?

I imagined it, a third, itinerant part of me, digitised into a billion bits, bouncing through the air or doing whatever it is digital bits do. How far into space do bits travel? How do they avoid bumping into each other, or is it all right if that happens? Maybe my voice, and my mother's voice, and who knows how many voices from all those conversations I'd never be a part of, were up there now – squashed in invisible togetherness between the snowy clouds. The starry sky. The moon.

Notes on the Editors

Jackie Kay was born in Edinburgh and brought up in Glasgow. Her debut poetry collection, *The Adoption Papers*, was published in 1991. Her first novel, *Trumpet*, published in 1998, was awarded the Guardian Fiction Prize and short-listed for the International Impac Dublin Literary Award. Other books include two collections of short stories, *Why Don't You Stop Talking* (2002) and *Wish I Was Here* (2006), which won her the British Book Awards Decibel Writer of the Year. Her collection for children, *Red, Cherry Red* (2008), won the CLPE award. Her memoir *Red Dust Road* was published last year to critical acclaim. Her latest book, *Fiere* (2011), is a Poetry Book Society Recommendation. She lives in Manchester and was awarded an MBE for services to literature in 2006.

Kachi A. Ozumba is a Nigerian-born novelist and short-story writer. He won the Arts Council England's Decibel Penguin Prize in 2006 and a Commonwealth Short Story Prize in 2009. His debut novel, *The Shadow of a Smile* (2009), was short-listed for the Commonwealth Writers' Prize and for the Royal Society of Literature Ondaatje Prize for a distinguished work of fiction, non-fiction or poetry, evoking the spirit of a place. He lives in Newcastle.

Notes on the Authors

Ahnaf Abdul was born and raised in Malaysia, and spent two years in Singapore before coming to the UK. Although his haphazard approach to reading is best described as 'Oxfam-oriented', he particularly enjoys myths and fairytales, and hopes to eventually rework some classic Malay tales into English. In the meantime, his evil twin can be found at Oxford, studying Law.

Grete Brewer-Bakken was born and raised in California, where she earned her undergraduate degree in Literature and Creative Writing from UC Santa Cruz. Writing is her true love; she has dreamed of being a published author since she was a child. Other hobbies include playing the piano, hanging out with her dog and two cats, reading voraciously, and watching movies with a good dose of horror. Grete lives in Newcastle upon Tyne, where she is completing her Master of Arts in Creative Writing.

Sin-yan Gloria Chan studied MA in Translation Studies at the University of Birmingham. As a Hong Konger coming from a former British colony, she is so eager to experience British culture and see if the 'real' Britain resembles what she imagined. Of course, reality always differs from imagination and she has experienced more than just decency and the majestic British accent. In fact, a lot of funny little things, such as Brummie, have changed her perception of Britain, but at the same time, made her stay in Birmingham more enjoyable. By writing short stories she hopes to share laughter and happiness with those who also love enjoying life with a sense of humour and wittiness.

Alan Islas-Cital was born in Ensenada, a small port town in the north of Mexico, near the California border. He has always loved to read, and this passion has greatly influenced his life. In part, he studied Electrical Engineering because of an early infatuation with science fiction, particularly the nostalgic writings of Ray Bradbury. His first job took him to the lakes of Oklahoma to build and test sonar units. Afterwards, he continued with this interest in underwater acoustics and obtained a scholarship to study a PhD at the University of Birmingham, starting in autumn 2007.

Ayodele Morocco-Clarke is a Nigerian lawyer and writer of mixed heritage who likes to describe herself as stubbornly unconventional. She has been adjudged runner-up of the International Students' Awards for two consecutive years and is the editor of the book review blog, *Critical Literature Review* (www.critical literaturereview.blogspot.com). Her written works have appeared in many literary journals and anthologies, including *African Roar*, *The New Black Magazine*, *Saraba Magazine*, *Hackwriters*, *Author Africa 2009* and *Sphere Literary Magazine*. Ayodele is currently finishing work on a short-story collection of her own and has started work on a novel which she hopes to publish in the not-too-distant future.

Ahmed Elsayed Fetit hails from Egypt and is a student at the University of Birmingham.

Meleika Gooneratne is a final-year medical student at St George's, University of London, having transferred for clinical school after doing her preclinical Medicine degree at Cambridge. She loves being outdoors and daydreams of working in humanitarian settings, providing medical care in makeshift clinics out in the field and writing in the evenings by the light of a lamp to the grunts and murmurs of surrounding wildlife. Being from Sri Lanka, a country rocked by civil war and poverty, makes this a very important goal for her. Her most recent and exciting news has been being proposed to by the male protagonist in her story – it was after the story was submitted, so she presumes the flattery worked.

Muhammad Idzwan Husaini is a third-year medical student from Malaysia. While his interest in Medicine has robbed him of the chance to study Creative Writing formally, he blogs at eyesonbothsides.blogspot.com to make sure the passion remains alive. His interests include literature, performing arts, drawing, TV and films, history, travelling and issues related to politics, race, religion, youth, sexuality and AIDS. He complains about the weather in Newcastle half the time while the other half is spent talking and rambling, both of which are mostly to himself.

Eric Kalunga has just completed a Masters programme at Durham University. Before that he was working as a journalist. He loves writing prose and is interested in meeting other writers who share the same dream of establishing a career in writing. He hails from Tanzania.

Rebecca Brianne Lever was born and grew up in Spartanburg, South Carolina. She attended Spartanburg High School where she played football, rode horses, and started writing in a Creative Writing class. Now she attends the University of St Andrews where she studies Environmental Biology and Geography and is involved in the Ballroom Society, the Town Chorus, and the Ultimate Frisbee Club.

David Molloy is an Australian-born writer and performer, who has recently graduated with a Bachelor of Creative Arts (Dean's Scholar) from the University of Wollongong. He has an active engagement with the arts in a number of disciplines, including theatre, film and music. In the last four years, David has performed in international festivals and in numerous bands, and he has directed his own written plays on stage. He recently attained his citizenship of the United Kingdom, and is eager to pursue a life and career there in the future. He enjoys hard rock, witty banter and leaping off things.

Zoé Perrenoud was born and grew up in Lausanne, Switzerland. In 2006, she travelled to North Wales to study for a BA in English with Creative Writing at Bangor University, following on with an MA in Creative

Writing in 2009. One of her poems was included in the *Aesthetica Creative Works Annual 2009* and several of her texts have appeared in student publications. Her hobbies include reading, sewing and dancing.

Adji Hafiz Sjadzali was born in South Jakarta and grew up on its outskirts. The school he went to was a local Islamic school called Dian Didaktika where he stayed put through to middle school. He then had the privilege to up the ante in Jakarta International School. Having been immersed in an international environment he made the big leap and did his International Baccalaureate diploma in St Clare's College in Oxford. He then studied Business Management with European Studies at the University of Exeter. In his spare time he takes his camera out for a stroll, weather permitting. Otherwise he enjoys cooking and spoiling himself with good food.

Lucille Valentine was born and raised in South Africa during the apartheid years, a time of silences. Her father is a farmer and when she first went off to study she thought that she needed to do something practical, useful. So she studied Chemical Engineering. Then she did Computer Science. Two careers and two children later, having followed her husband to the UK, she studied Creative Writing. Thank goodness. She loves words, she loves the sound they make as they hit the page and then try and escape, dragging her with them.